FOREWOF

From its foundation as a pilot theatre project in
responded to the developments in the field of Reminiscence work and pioneered the
use of arts-based activities in many different settings.

Age Exchange is perhaps best known for its touring Reminiscence Theatre
productions, its Reminiscence Centre in London and its national training services,
but the Reminiscence Project operating in hospitals and residential homes has also
played a vital role in broadening the range and accessibility of our activities.

Caroline Osborn co-ordinated the Reminiscence Project throughout Greater
London during its first five years, developing the health and social service
application of our work and building up our professional training programme.

Twenty freelance Reminiscence Project workers have tried out innovative
approaches to running group sessions tailored to the needs of particular
participants in over one hundred and fifty placements across Greater London and
beyond.

Caroline's work in bringing this tremendous wealth of experience together
in THE REMINISCENCE HANDBOOK is a major addition to the literature now
available to help those who are just beginning reminiscence work as well as to
those who are already actively involved in running reminiscence sessions, but who
are always on the lookout for good ideas. The suggestions in this handbook will
provide material for an enormous variety and number of reminiscence
programmes.

For Caroline's invaluable contribution during her five years with the
Reminiscence Project, as well as for this excellent new book, I thank her most
sincerely.

Pam Schweitzer, Artistic Director, Age Exchange

CONTENTS

I. INTRODUCTION

1. BACKGROUND

Remembering things or people from the past is an everyday occurrence for many people of all ages. The past is often shared with friends or reflected on in private. As a formal activity, reminiscence is now a well-established means of encouraging communication and understanding in most places where older people gather together. The purpose of this book is to provide a source of reminiscence ideas for staff who work with older people to draw upon.

Reminiscence activities take place in settings where older people are together to live or by day in order to receive support for their lives, as well as in adult education centres, libraries and local museums. The ideas in the book and the suggestions in the **INTRODUCTION** can be applied to reminiscence in care settings (residential homes, day centres, hospital wards, continuing care homes, nursing homes, day hospitals) as well as in places where people meet to reminisce but are not receiving other forms of care (clubs, libraries, adult education classes and museums).

Some of the reminiscence which takes place in such places as day centres, day hospitals and continuing care residential or nursing homes occurs spontaneously with little or no preparation. But, as with any care activity, the spontaneous ways of doing things are not the only ones nor necessarily the best. This book aims to encourage staff to plan and monitor their reminiscence work, to select the most appropriate approach for their purpose, and above all to bring variety to their reminiscence activities.

Carefully planned reminiscence activities also flourish in many places. This book is written with experienced staff of such settings in mind to support them in their work of running activities by suggesting ideas and approaches which may be new to them. The business of having constant new stimulating ideas is sometimes difficult to find the energy for. The ideas here should help.

The phrase 'older people' covers a thirty-year age span and enormous differences of experience related to sex, culture, class, age and personality. Reminiscence is a valuable way of acknowledging both the differences and the similarities between people's experience. Through reminiscence people can enjoy the satisfaction of discovering that others have similar memories to theirs. They can also strengthen their own identity through recognising the particularly individual features of their own life. A skilled reminiscence worker should try to ensure that people have the experience of both.

The members of some reminiscence groups are in

charge of their own activities and involved in writing, researching and educating. On the other hand reminiscence is also an extremely useful way of interacting with people with considerable levels of mental frailty. People using this book will need to select, experiment with and adapt the activities to suit the interests and skills of the people they are working with.

The ideas included in this book have evolved through the work of Age Exchange under the inspiring leadership of Pam Schweitzer., In particular they reflect the work of the Reminiscence Project which promotes reminiscence activities with older people and the staff who work with them in hospitals, residential homes, nursing homes, day centres and clubs. Most of the ideas included in the book have been used many times in such settings. Much of the credit for the ideas should go to the many creative reminiscence workers who have been associated with Age Exchange, to the enthusiastic nurses and care staff with whom we have

worked, and to the older people who have been so willing to join in with all sorts of reminiscence activities and have helped us develop and experiment.

This introduction provides some practical advice about setting up, running and reviewing reminiscence sessions. The section titled **'TYPES OF ACTIVITY'** explains how to approach the different kinds of exercises suggested The main part of the book consists of theme based **'IDEAS SECTIONS'** in which many different ways of stimulating memories are described. An appendix called **'WAYS OF ASKING QUESTIONS'** is included, as it is important that people leading reminiscence activities are skilled in prompting and asking questions appropriately. A list of books and articles for further reading is provided in an appendix. The work of John Adams, Joanna Bornat, Peter Coleman Faith Gibson and Pam Schweitzer is particularly useful for people wanting to explore the place of reminiscence and the experience of others in more detail.

2. THE BENEFITS FOR OLDER PEOPLE

There are many arguments for reminiscence having a place in the daily lives of older people who are dependent on others to structure their time and provide them with stimulation. Many of the same arguments hold good for independent older people too.

To my mind, one of the main arguments for reminiscence is that remembering the past is a normal activity which we should give people an opportunity to

take part in if they wish. People who are no longer living in their own homes surrounded by mementos, or people who rarely go out and have few old friends, probably do not have much chance of spontaneous reminiscence unless the people caring for them make special opportunities. Informal conversations about their lives and more organised reminiscence group activities provide the opportunity for people who need some help or encouragement or prompting to recall and share their history.

Reminiscence is a very important way of knowing who we are. It has been suggested that knowing and understanding our roots and life history are the basis for our sense of identity and personal confidence. It is particularly important that we support and encourage people in their task of recalling who they are if they are finding it difficult to remember for themselves, either because of mental frailty or because they are receiving care which fails to preserve fully their individuality.

Another justification for reminiscence is that for people who are not very active in the present, the past may provide the most vivid topic of conversation and is therefore an excellent focus for social activity with other people of all ages. One of the great strengths of reminiscence is that it can be used as a focus for a range of different enjoyable activities, from straightforward socialising to writing, painting, making performing, and teaching. Outings and practivities such as cooking, gardening, cleaning, can stimulate and be stimulated by memories. ctivities with people of different generations or ounds can have a reminiscence starting point or outcome.

Reminiscence also provides opportunities for positive achievement to people who have degrees of mental or physical frailty, whose present lives may be characterised by decline and failure. The long term memory, which reminiscence uses, frequently survives after other physical and mental capacities decline. Reminiscence activities should always be designed so that people succeed, so that their abilities are used, so that people get a sense of achievement from taking part.

In a real sense reminiscence provides an opportunity for people to have something which they are in charge of and are expert in. They decide whether to share, keep private, or elaborate memories about their own lives, about which we know less than they do. Being an expert and having other people interested in you is a source of great satisfaction for everyone. For many older people this is a particularly rare occurrence in a society which puts so little value on old age and promotes so many negative images of ageing.

Reminiscence can also be the means by which people develop increased confidence in themselves and learn new skills. Groups based in adult education settings, community centres or local history projects may go on to learn how to use word processors, how to mount exhibitions, how to do creative writing or acting. Public speaking and community involvement can also become part of their involvement in reminiscence.

These reasons, plus the enjoyment and satisfaction that so many older people so evidently get from being involved in reminiscence, justify the time and attention which should be devoted to it.

3. THE BENEFITS FOR STAFF

Anyone who has tried to encourage reminiscence work among care staff has been told, time and again, 'we do this anyway'. This is, of course, true. Recalling the past forms part of the informal conversation between people of all ages, between older people and between carers and older people. In care situations informal reminiscence discussions are a very positive way of interacting between people. More formal reminiscence however provides a context for involving people in creative activities which have been considered and planned and for setting targets and monitoring their achievement. If reminiscence is seen only as a spontaneous activity, then there is little incentive for the care worker to take seriously the development of the necessary skills or plan and monitor activities.

From the point of view of staff, reminiscence is a major way of appreciating the individuality of people and being reminded that they are real people with a long personal and social past. That in itself is a major justification. Staff have frequently reported to me how much reminiscence helps them relate to the people they look after as individuals with a life time of experiences and personal strengths rather than as people who need this or that level of help because of their disabilities. As a member of staff it is much harder to think only in terms of 'the woman in the green chair who needs taking to the toilet every two hours' when you know something about her life and have shared vivid memories with her.

In addition, staff often discover that they develop skills in communication, running groups, organising

activities, or generating creative ideas which are a considerable source of additional job satisfaction and enjoyment.

In many residential homes and other continuing care settings, time spent talking to residents is easily squeezed out by physical care tasks. Establishing reminiscence as a formal activity rather than as something to be fitted in other tasks permitting is a way of ensuring that adequate time is made for it.

However reminiscence enthusiasts should beware of ageist stereotyping which implies that all older people always enjoy remembering the past and that this is all they want to do. Reminiscence is one of many activities in which older people may choose to take part. Their views about what they do or do not want to do should always be respected.

4. STARTING REMINISCENCE ACTIVITIES

One of the strengths of reminiscence is that leadership skills can be developed as part of the role of a care worker as well as by people whose starting point is in the arts, in teaching, in oral history, in working with groups. Whatever your starting point, the most important qualities you need to have to run good reminiscence sessions are a real interest in what people have to say, confidence in facilitating group activities, and a commitment to making the occasion stimulating.

It is advisable to be honest with yourself about whether reminiscence is for you or not. One test is to consider whether you like reminiscing about your own life. If you do, then you are likely to think that it is a normal, positive thing to do. If you would rather not think about your own past, then you are unlikely to be comfortable running a reminiscence group. In the latter situation, you will probably convey the message that reminiscence is an unwarranted intrusion into people's privacy, into things that they would rather forget.

As a reminiscence worker, you have to be interested in the details of everyday life, in people who led ordinary lives in ordinary ways, as well as in the reminiscence 'stars' - the people who have done extraordinary things and can tell a good story about them.

Confidence about running groups comes with practice and self awareness. "*Groupwork with the Elderly* "by Mike Bender, Andrew Norris and Paulette Bauckham (see book list for details) is a valuable resource with useful guidance and suggestions for beginners and more experienced people. Background knowledge about the lives of the people who are now old can be gained by reading published oral and local history material and by remembering what people tell you.

Before reminiscence activities can start, the reminiscence worker has several things to consider: the purpose of the activity, the number and length of the sessions, how to recruit participants, where the session

is to be held, and how to monitor and review. In all care settings support of managers and colleagues is essential so that time can be made available, interruptions avoided and recognition given to the importance of the activity both for the participants and for the staff running it.

The purpose of the activity needs to be decided. The previous sections which discuss the benefits for older people and for staff suggest some ways of thinking about this. The sessions may be mainly social, or they may be part of a programme of activities designed to develop or use the skills of the particular participants, or the sessions may work towards an exhibition or a book as an end product. For a particular individual, involvement in reminiscence may be included in the plan for their care as a way of understanding them better, or in order to help them join in with others, or to promote social and communication skills.

Closely linked with decisions about the purpose, is consideration about the number of sessions to be held. In some places this may be determined by adult education terms or by resources, if a special worker is being paid for. In other places a period of time each week is programmed as being for reminiscence on an ongoing basis. One way of sharing out scarce time is to propose a block of sessions, say six or ten, with one group of participants and then form another group with different participants for another block of sessions.

Consideration needs to be given to how the activity is going to be described so that potential participants can make a decision about whether they want to join in or not. In a club or adult education class attendance probably depends upon the publicity reaching the right people. In a residential home or hospital ward there is a group of people at hand who can be told about the activity and encouraged to join in. In some places taking part in a reminiscence group may be part of the care plan for particular individuals.

It is useful to plan a form of words to describe the activity. Phrases such as 'a chance to talk about the past/the old days' or 'a meeting to share memories' are sometimes used. Alternatively, think of an appropriate name to call the group, such as the 'Reminiscence Club', or the 'Memories Group'.

It is important to think carefully before deciding how large the group should be and how long a session should last. In many residential care settings, six or eight group members and three-quarters of an hour to an hour seems to be about right, particularly if people are accustomed to joining in with group activities. If the participants are not accustomed to participating in activities or have some degree of mental frailty then half an hour may be quite long enough. In some clubs, adult education classes and sometimes day hospitals there may be little choice about the number of participants and the group may have to be much larger - ten or even twenty people - and the session time much longer - a couple of hours.

When working with people with a high degree of mental frailty, who are scarcely able to speak and have a very short attention span, experiment with a group of two or three at most and reduce the length of time to little more than ten minutes. Some moderately mentally frail people successfully join a larger, longer group if the other participants are more able.

Time to plan and review the activities is essential. Keep notes on each session: who attended, what was discussed, what resources were useful, how the session went, what you can learn for another time, what you plan to do next time, and what needs to be prepared. Review the sessions regularly.

Choose a quiet room or space with as few distractions as possible. Plan where people will sit so that they can see and hear each other and communicate. Try varying the seating arrangements from time to time and notice whether the differences alter the dynamics of the group. Try to hold the group in a room which makes it possible for people who have hearing loss to hear what others are saying as easily as possible. It is particularly difficult to hear in rooms which echo or which are far too large for the size of the group. Rooms where other activities are taking place at the same time are difficult to concentrate in.

Plan to avoid the interruptions of the medicine round or people being called away to do other things. This will mean carefully working out when the most appropriate time to hold the session is and when such interruptions can be avoided. In a two hour or longer session it may be appropriate to have a refreshment break half way through. Shorter sessions should not be interrupted, as serving and drinking tea breaks the concentration. Tea at the end of the session can be a good idea and often means that people continue talking informally while they drink. Refreshments at the beginning are sometimes used as an inducement to come to the session. If this is necessary, do put cups out of the way before starting properly. It is impossible to drink a cup of tea and demonstrate the use of a washboard at the same time.

5. CONFIDENTIALITY

Confidentiality is an important issue in reminiscence. Everyone needs to know that within the group their memories will be treated with respect, and that outside the group there will be no gossiping. Some groups draw up guidelines for group behaviour, confidentiality and mutual respect. Confidentiality needs to be treated seriously both by the people running the sessions and by the group members.

However, some forms of reminiscence activity such as writing, drawing, recording or acting, involve making memories public and you need to be sure that participants are prepared for this. You need to check carefully that people agree to their reminiscence material being included in publications or displays. Some people are concerned to keep private aspects of their life which others would regard as trivial, while others are quite happy to reveal the most personal things.

If you are running reminiscence activities in a care setting you should discuss with the manager and other staff whether you want to establish total confidentiality in all circumstances. You may wish to share insights which appear to shed light on behaviour in the present, or you may think that this is completely inappropriate. You certainly need to discuss in advance what to do if anything comes up in a reminiscence session which indicates that some form of abuse is taking place currently. In these circumstances you would probably want to say to the individual, and perhaps to the group, that something said is so important that it has to be passed on to someone in authority.

The situation is different and less clear cut if the members of the reminiscence group are totally in charge of their own lives. If you become concerned that someone is being abused by someone else, your first step would be to discuss your concern with the individual privately.

6. REMINISCENCE WORKERS AS 'OUTSIDERS'

In day and residential settings reminiscence activities are sometimes run by a visiting 'outsider' coming into a group. A visiting reminiscence worker might be someone from a community history or arts project or someone invited into a setting for a specific period or piece of work.

There are both advantages and disadvantages to being in this position. The fact that the reminiscence worker does not have other commitments within the setting which will take them away from the reminiscence activity is a distinct advantage compared to a busy care worker who has to make a place for reminiscence alongside other responsibilities. The outsider, if for instance they are a specialist reminiscence worker or arts worker, will have knowledge, experience and skills which are not always found in nursing or care workers in stimulating participation in arts activities or in working with groups. If they are part of a project, they may be able to forge links with other similar activities taking place elsewhere in the area.

The lack of prior knowledge about the participants, which might be thought to be a great disadvantage for an outsider, can also be turned into an advantage in some circumstances. Within settings, staff can fall into habits of communication with the old people they look after which presupposes a certain type of answer. For instance, if experience shows that someone rarely replies, the way they are talked to will carry that expectation. A reminiscence worker from outside is able to approach everyone afresh as a responsive adult and will not have any prior expectations. I have seen someone responding adult to adult to a question from a reminiscence worker who did not know her, to the amazement of watching staff who were about to say something to the effect of 'Don't bother with her, she never answers'.

The great disadvantage of reminiscence activities being undertaken by a visiting reminiscence worker in a residential or day setting is that the activity easily remains rather separate from the daily life of the people living in the home or attending the day centre. This can be overcome to some extent by arranging that the visiting reminiscence worker is joined by a permanent member of staff. But there is still a danger that reminiscence only takes place when the reminiscence worker is visiting, instead of there being a link between formal activities and frequent informal conversations.

As one of the most positive aspects of reminiscence is the opportunity it provides for people receiving a high level of care to be seen by staff as real people, it is important that reminiscence in care settings is not only undertaken by visiting reminiscence workers. In order for reminiscence to help reduce the depersonalisation which can happen in care settings, staff need to be fully involved.

The model promoted by the **AGE EXCHANGE REMINISCENCE PROJECT** acknowledges the role of outsiders as well as the importance for reminiscence to be very much part of the everyday life of care settings. The project works in local authority residential homes and day centres, hospital wards and day hospitals, and in private and voluntary settings. It involves visiting reminiscence workers working in partnership with permanent staff introducing reminiscence for the first time or sharing new ideas and approaches and then withdrawing to leave responsibility for undertaking reminiscence work with the permanent staff. Continued support and further ideas are available at the **AGE EXCHANGE REMINISCENCE CENTRE** in London. Other projects around the country work in similar ways.

7. ISSUES FOR VISITING REMINISCENCE WORKERS

There are particular issues to be considered if you are going into a care setting as an outside reminiscence worker. You need to be clear that the expectations that everyone has of you are the same as yours. You should agree in advance how many sessions you will be running and what their purpose is. It is essential to have a link person at the setting with whom you can discuss both minor and major difficulties and decisions.

An important area for advanced discussion is whether any of the staff based in the setting are to take part in the sessions. If you are to have a role in passing on skills to them, you need to think about how you are going to do that and allow for time together to discuss, plan and feedback to each other. If staff are present only as observers, decide how many observers you want to have, and what you expect of an observer - complete silence or some involvement - and what they are going to do with what they observe. If no other staff are to be present at all, you need to discuss what to do in emergencies such as a group member feeling ill or needing help to go to the toilet. Decide in advance how you should deal with such situations.

As a visiting reminiscence worker you need to agree before you start how many group members you will be working with, how they will be selected or told about the activity, and whether you want the same people at each session. Visiting reminiscence workers sometimes have difficulties because they do not know which group members will turn up from session to session. Either far too many people are present, some perhaps wheeled in without any explanation, or too few and one may suspect that some subtle sabotage is taking place on the part of the permanent staff.

It is advisable therefore to decide before you begin whether you will invite people to the group by talking to them yourself individually or in a group or through other forms of publicity or whether you will leave the inviting (and reminding) to the staff. In the latter situation you should discuss the basis for the invitation or selection and ask for a list of names in advance.

If the group members need help to get to the room where the reminiscence session is going to take place, discuss in advance whether you have a role in helping or not. If you do help, you may find that you spend up to quarter of an hour getting the group members together. This time needs to be allowed for.

The experience of the Age Exchange Reminiscence Project is that clear expectations and organisation is essential when going in to a care setting as a visiting reminiscence worker. Despite every effort, communications within care settings which employ many staff do cause difficulties which have to be handled with patience and understanding.

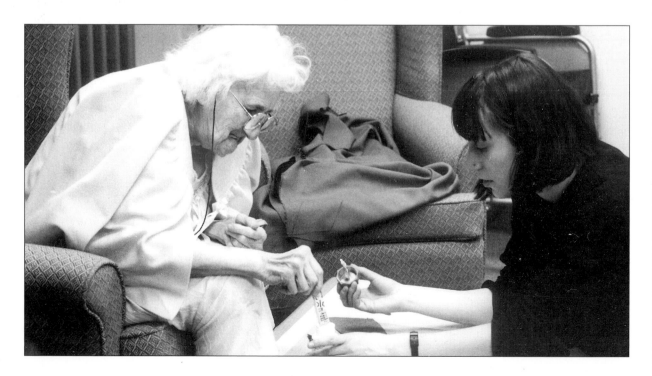

8. RUNNING REMINISCENCE SESSIONS

I have written this book in the belief that there can be more to reminiscence sessions than sitting around talking week after week and that older people frequently and enthusiastically respond to the challenge of different sorts of activities. If reminiscence group leaders are bold enough to experiment using some of the ideas suggested, the quality of the group experience will be enhanced and the process of remembering will be more exciting.

Before the start of each session, prepare yourself thoroughly, so the session is not confused. If you are using the ideas in this book, read through the relevant **IDEAS SECTION** and decide what you are going to cover in the session. Make sure that you understand what you are going to do and have any resources or materials ready. Prepare yourself by thinking of prompts in advance.

Organise the room in advance so that people sit where they can see and hear each other - a circle is preferable. Plan where you as leader are going to sit in relation to people with particular needs. For instance someone who is deaf may need to be next to you so that you can repeat things to them or write them down.

Do not rush from activity to activity but give the group time to reflect and expand on their initial memories. Some people take a long time to recover their memories, put something into words and respond. They may be ready to make a contribution ten minutes after they first started thinking, so it would be a pity if you had gone on to something else. People reminisc-

ing often express the most satisfaction about remembering the things they did not know they remembered. We all have some well rehearsed stories we have told many times; what is really exciting is to surprise oneself with a memory or a detail that one had not recalled before. It takes time to reach these memories.

Notice how you talk to people - avoid questions which people cannot answer, avoid 'closed' questions which only need a one word answer, use 'open' questions (see the section: **WAYS OF ASKING QUESTIONS**). Respect what people say and do not use a patronising tone of voice, tease or make fun of people. Do not tell people what they remember (ie *'everyone remembers the blitz'*). Do not talk too much yourself or show off your knowledge. Do value what people say and take an interest in everyone's contribution.

Encourage people to talk to each other and discourage them from addressing only you. You can do this by asking permission to repeat one person's comments loud enough for everyone to hear. You can make connections between different people's reminiscences. An example of this would be making sure that two people knew that they had both lived in the same area and encourage them to share memories: talking to Miss Brown, *"You said that you used to live in Glasgow. Do you remember that Mrs Smith told us last week that she lived as a child in Glasgow? Why don't you ask her what part she lived in?."* Another way of encouraging people to talk to each other which is possible with some groups is to spend some time in each session in pairs, talking or examining objects or pictures.

9. PLANNING THE SESSIONS

This book is arranged in topics which correspond to fairly universal aspects of growing up and young adult life. Each section describes ideas which will take greatly varying lengths of time from a few minutes to many weeks. It is not suggested that you work through each idea, but that you select and adapt those which seem appropriate to your situation.

It is important to have a focus for each session, so that people know what sorts of memories are going to feature. Some groups will have a programme of several weeks planned in advance. In others, the next topic will suggest itself from session to session and planning far ahead will not be appropriate. Some participants will be able to prepare themselves in advance and will be able to start the process of remembering on their own before the session. They can also be encouraged and supported to look out relevant photographs or objects of their own to bring to the session.

One way of choosing the topics for a series of sessions is to go through life events roughly chronologically. The topics in this book are arranged in that way. However, it may be appropriate to ask the group members to make their own suggestions or a subject may come up in one session which provides the topic for the next. A different approach is to have a common theme for all the sessions. Memories of the local area is an obvious choice for a group who originated and have stayed in the same area.

Another approach is to relate the choice of topic to something in the present. For instance, you could prepare people who are to go to the seaside by remembering childhood visits to the sea, or people

whose living arrangements are changing by encouraging them to talk about other times they have moved house. The choice of topic can also be related to the seasons, festivals, special public occasions such as anniversaries related to the war or the royal family.

It is a good idea to have a clear beginning and end to each session. Remind people at the start of each session what the activity is and how long it will last. Some activities are particularly suitable to focus people's attention to the theme and are labelled as such in the **IDEAS SECTIONS**. Other activities are more appropriate as endings as they involve summing up or giving everyone a last comment or relating memories of the past to life in the present. Such activities are also identified. If you are working with people who are mentally frail, it is important to start and end in the same way each time, so some familiar rituals are established.

Advance planning should take into account any equipment needed. It is a great help to accumulate useful reminiscence resources such as books, pictures and objects, so that you do not have to find them from scratch each time you need them. There are many suggestions in the **IDEAS SECTIONS** of objects which are useful reminiscence triggers. Your reminiscence cupboard or box can also usefully contain drawing materials, tapes and a tape recorder.

Your planning notes should cover the following areas:

- **The topic**
- **Opening activity**
- **Main activity**
- **Closing activity**
- **Resources needed**
- **Note of anything you specially want to achieve that session**
- **Who is going to do what if more than one facilitator is involved.**

10. REVIEWING AND EVALUATING

It is often difficult after a reminiscence session to make time to keep a record of what took place. If you are a care worker you may feel that the first priority is to take people to other rooms, tidy up, attend to tasks

which have been left waiting. Whatever your role, you may be tired from the concentrated work of facilitating a group. However, if you do not find time very soon after the session to make a clear and useful record, it will be very difficult to assess whether you are doing a good job or not, to gain in skill and learn from experience, and to know what the participants are getting out of it.

These are some of the things which should be recorded:

- **factual information about the date and time of the group and who attended**

- **factual information about the subject matter of the session, the session plan, the triggers or resources used and the ways in which they were successful or not**

- **comments about practical things which contributed to the success of the group (for instance, an arrangement of chairs which enabled everyone to see each other)**

- **comments about practical things which detracted from its success (for instance, a noisy machine outside which meant that it was difficult to hear)**

- **information about the group dynamics which should be maintained or altered with suggestions about how to handle them next time.**

- **The purpose of the sessions and evidence that it fulfilled its purpose**

- **Comments on how well the leader managed**

- **Plans for the future.**

As with all record keeping, a clear distinction should be made between fact and opinion. The records should show the evidence for your comments. It is not appropriate, for instance, to write *'Mrs S was in a bad mood'*. If you feel it was relevant to the session you can record what Mrs S did and what she said, but not what you think she was feeling unless she told you herself. Your records should be consistent with the guidelines on confidentiality of the workplace.

11. COMMON PROBLEMS

A common problem in reminiscence is difficulty in dealing with participants who talk too much. The problem often arises because the group leader hesitates about being sufficiently assertive. It is important to value and acknowledge the over-talkative person's contributions, and then ask them to listen to what someone else has got to say. Explain firmly that everyone needs to have a turn. Activities which very clearly involve people taking turns are a particularly useful way of structuring and limiting the contributions of over talkative people.

A frequent anxiety of people starting to run reminiscence activities is what to do if someone cries. This concern is often closely linked to attitudes towards emotional expression prevailing at the workplace. If very little emotion is permitted, then workers probably have little experience of dealing confidently with crying, or anger, when it does occur. Often this anxiety, though expressed in terms of care for the older person, may also be about the worker's own worries over their ability to cope with someone else's sadness. In fact, crying in reminiscence is rarer than people think,

though it does happen.

Some staff express a fear that reminiscence activities might somehow unearth deeply buried pain and leave people in distress. This is extremely unlikely. In general, people do not share unhappy memories or feelings unless they feel comfortable doing so. The purpose of most reminiscence sessions is to use past memories to facilitate recall, communication and other activities, not to uncover secrets or dig up an unhappy past.

People do have experiences which they feel emotional about and these cannot be avoided, nor would this necessarily be desirable. It is normal to feel emotional about some memories. People may also voice a realistic sadness about their current situation. A reminiscence session may be an appropriate opportunity to share emotions. Sometimes however someone may abruptly change the subject or stop talking and this may be a sign that they do not want to say any more. You should listen for this and respect it.

If someone does become distressed or sheds tears, do not panic.

Take a few moments to think what to do.

- A good approach is to take your lead from the person in distress.
- Acknowledge that sometimes remembering the past is sad and enquire whether they want to go on participating.
- They may want to be left in peace for a while, in which case switch the focus to other members of the group.
- They may want an arm round the shoulder or a pat on the hand.
- They may want to leave the room.
- Enlist the other members of the group to help you.

After the end of the group you may need to offer that person some private time. You may also need some support yourself from your supervisor or manager and you should not hesitate to ask for it.

12. REMINISCENCE WITH MENTALLY FRAIL PEOPLE

The experience of Age Exchange is that many people with quite high degrees of mental frailty can participate successfully in appropriate reminiscence activities. Many writers of reminiscence, notably Faith Gibson, confirm this view. The Age Exchange Reminiscence Project is frequently told by staff members how surprised they are by the positive response of elderly mentally frail people whom the staff thought would not be able to join in. It is important not to underestimate a mentally frail person's capacity to concentrate, to contribute, to stay sitting down even, given the right activity and atmosphere.

Faith Gibson has observed increased sociability and increased conversation by mentally frail people and increased desire on the part of the carers to know about people's lives and to respond to the needs of the mentally frail people in less stereotyped ways. She emphasises the importance of encouraging staff to believe and try to understand what people say rather than reject comments which cannot be immediately understood as the product of confused behaviour.

In our experience it is not necessary as a matter of course to exclude mentally frail people who are very restless. Some find it possible to sit and join in with an interesting group and find relief from their anxious wandering for a time. If that is not the case, it is useful to decide how many times you will ask someone to stay (perhaps twice); otherwise the people who are willing to join in may get less attention than someone wanting to leave.

Reminiscence can sometimes provide ways of interacting with people with very high levels of mental frailty who seem scarcely able to respond at all to speech. For such people it is useful to think about things to taste, touch or smell which might make links for them with the past. Velvet and silk are interesting to touch, lavender water or moth balls familiar smells, raspberries or seed cake might be appropriate tastes. There are other suggestions throughout the **IDEAS SECTIONS** of this book. You may not be able to tell whether people are making connections or not, but if they respond at all you are at least extending the range of experience available to them.

A different approach useful for working with people with mental frailty, as well as others, is compiling a life story book. Making a life story book does not have the social benefits of being part of a group, but it does involve valuable one-to-one contact. The process involves close personal attention, which in itself can be a positive experience for someone, particularly if they receive little attention in other ways. Working with people on their life story has been found to be an excellent way of helping people who are very frustrated or angry, as well as people who are difficult to know because of their mental confusion.

In a life story book as much detail of someone's life as possible is recorded and preserved in order to help someone remember who they are and enable others to relate to them as a person rather than a list of 'needs'. The material for the book is gathered from the person as far as possible and expanded by information from relatives and friends and careful research. Relevant pictures and personal photographs can enliven the writing. The inclusion of a family tree will enable carers and the older person to understand who family members are and how they relate to each other. Maps recording moves and change are another method of varying the way information is presented.

The book can then become a valued possession of the older person and a focus for conversation with staff and family visitors. It is a particularly valuable record if the person's ability to remember decreases over time.

II. TYPES OF ACTIVITIES

This section lists and describes activities according to their type. The IDEAS SECTIONS which form the main part of the book are arranged around themes (Home Life, Schooldays etc.). Each theme can be explored using many different types of activity.

TYPES OF ACTIVITIES

- 1 Asking round the group
- 2 Display making
- 3 Drama ideas
- 4 Drawing
- 5 Handling objects
- 6 Making a list
- 7 Maps
- 8 Music and sounds
- 9 Outings
- 10 Practical activities
- 11 Prompted reminiscence
- 12 Read a quotation
- 13 Showing round
- 14 Story telling
- 15 Then and now
- 16 Things learned by heart
- 17 Touch, taste and smell
- 18 Using pictures

1. ASKING ROUND THE GROUP

Asking everyone in the group to respond briefly to a question is a good way of limiting excessively talkative people and encouraging quiet ones. Even people who do not normally speak can sometimes manage to give a one word answer. You can readily move to fuller memories by inviting people to expand on brief answers.

A.   The leader asks everyone in the group the same or a similar question and requests a one word or very short answer. Sometimes this is a useful way of starting a session and getting some initial information. For example ask everyone where they went to school and   you will get an idea of the geographical spread.

B.   Asking around the group is also a way of encouraging imagination. For example: have (or pretend to have) a small brown paper bag and ask everyone in turn: *'When you were a child what sort of sweets would you have wanted there to be in this bag?'*. Or hand round a doll and say to everyone in turn: *'If this had been your doll, what would you have wanted to call it?'*

2. DISPLAY MAKING

Sometimes reminiscence groups like to work towards a display to put on the wall or on a table to share with other people. Several of the ideas described could be included in a display, particularly writing, listing, story telling and drawing activities. Objects could also be included.

A map marked with the relevant places makes a good basis for a display. Use strings to show where people used to live, for instance, accompanied by pieces of writing, pictures, postcards. A display can be used as the starting point for reminiscence or as a conclusion.

3. DRAMA IDEAS

There are many ways of using spontaneous drama in reminiscence, many of them lasting only a minute or so and not involving any movement. Sometimes people will hardly realise that they are taking part in a drama activity. Once you are comfortable using these ideas you will begin to see opportunities for yourself. There will always be times when an idea does not work, so be prepared to pass on to something else.

TYPES OF ACTIVITIES

The first four examples of drama ideas use words rather than actions and work particularly well for arguments or other forms of heated exchange. Idea 'E' is a suggestion about using mime. Of course more elaborate improvised or prepared drama can be very successfully based on reminiscence.

A.   In the context of a discussion, the group leader speaks as if he or she were someone else (**EXAMPLE:** a strict school teacher saying *'Sit still at the back there!'*) and looks for a spontaneous one or two word response from one of the reminiscers.
(**EXAMPLE:** *'it wasn't me Miss!'*).

B.   A slightly more prepared version of the previous example: the group leader says *'If I were a strict school teacher and I said, "Sit still at the back there!" what would you reply?'* and then encourages people to make a suggestion to which the group leader makes a further reply. Continue the interchange for a minute or two.

C.   This is a rather more elaborate version, but still only lasts a couple of minutes. The group leader asks people to take roles related to a situation which has been remembered and then play out a dialogue, discussion or argument. For instance, one person speaks for the teacher, another for a parent, another for a child. They may be able to think of what to say to each other in the remembered situation. Alternatively, others in the group can be encouraged to join in by suggesting what the different characters would have said. The person playing the part then repeats the suggestions in role.

D.   Another version of the same: the group leader speaks for all the roles but only uses words provided by the group members. The leader has to invite suggestions about what would be said next after each contribution.

EXAMPLE:

Leader, setting the scene,
  'I am a cross mother because my sixteen year old daughter has come home late. What would the mother say to the daughter?'
Contribution from the reminiscence group,
  'I told you to be back at 10.30, why are you late?'.
Leader repeating,
  'I told you to be back at 10.30, why are you late?'.
Leader going on,
  'What answer would the daughter give?'.
Someone in the reminiscence group suggests,
  ' The bus didn't come.'
Leader repeats this and asks what the mother might have said next and so on.

This exercise can be extended to include what the characters are thinking but not saying, e.g someone in the group suggests the real explanation for lateness and how the daughter <u>really</u> feels about it.

E. The leader mimes an activity and asks others to guess what he or she is doing (this can be used to start off the theme). Then others are encouraged to mime something else to do with the theme.
EXAMPLE: everyone is encouraged to mime something to do with the work they once did.

The mime can be quite simple and brief or you could encourage it to go on longer and be accompanied by an explanation in words. For example, I once observed a former bricklayer finding it much easier to explain how to build a wall by using mime than by speaking. He mimed all the processes from unloading the bricks to mixing and putting the mortar on and so on even though he could not find the words to explain how to do it.

F. Puppets are another possibility. If you are good with your hands, make some appropriately dressed puppets to have available. Jointed puppets on sticks are easier to hold for people with stiff fingers than glove puppets. Encourage people to speak through the puppets.

4. DRAWING, PAINTING & COLLAGE

Making a visual image from memory provides prompts which tend to be different from those which might come to mind in talking. For instance, in order to draw a particular house one needs to know how many storeys it had, whether it was terraced or semi detached, what sort of roof it had, where the front door was, where on the front door the letter box was, etc.

In most of the drawing activities described, the process and the memories are more important than the quality of the drawing. 'Pin people' and assistance from labels and writing are quite acceptable. Whether the end product looks like a rough diagram or a crude picture, it will serve to help the reminiscence process while it is being made, and can be referred back to later as well.

A. Ask people to make a drawing or painting of a remembered scene or place either as a group or individual activity. Encourage them to remember and draw the details.

B. For people who cannot draw or for those for whom the act of drawing would inhibit the memory process, you can do the drawing for them. Ask them to describe to you how they want things drawn. You will need to ask detailed questions to make the drawing, which in turn will prompt their memories. You will need to resist making assumptions about what things looked like. Good subjects are:

- a particular room in a house they lived in
- a remembered street
- a market, a garden
- a seaside place
- clothes they wore
- a more detailed subject such as objects on the kitchen mantelpiece.

C.   The process described in **EXAMPLE 'B'** can be used as a group activity as well as an individual one. Use the same technique of asking what to put in the picture but include the suggestions of several people. For instance, a drawing of a garden might include a rose bed suggested by one person, a cabbage patch suggested by another, a banana tree suggested by someone else. It might include someone's mother hanging out washing on a line and someone else's mother doing the washing by the stream. When the picture is finished, discuss the different contributions with the group.

D.   A more elaborate picture using painting or collage might be the work of several weeks, following reminiscence discussions, research in picture books and careful preparation of materials. A group reminiscence collage might use paint, paper with various textures and colours, photocopied pictures, and materials such as cloth, knitting, lace, dried flowers, raffia - anything appropriate.

5. HANDLING OBJECTS

Old objects, contemporary but traditional objects, even modern objects are excellent reminiscence triggers and can be used in many different ways, so it is valuable to have access to a variety of objects to handle. It is very useful to assemble your own collection and the **IDEAS SECTIONS** provide plenty of suggestions. One or two relevant objects can make a great difference to the liveliness of a session.

Reminiscence Boxes containing objects to handle, pictures and reminiscence ideas sheets can be hired from Age Exchange; the list of available boxes is printed at the end of the book. Some other reminiscence projects and some local museums also have collections of objects which people can handle.

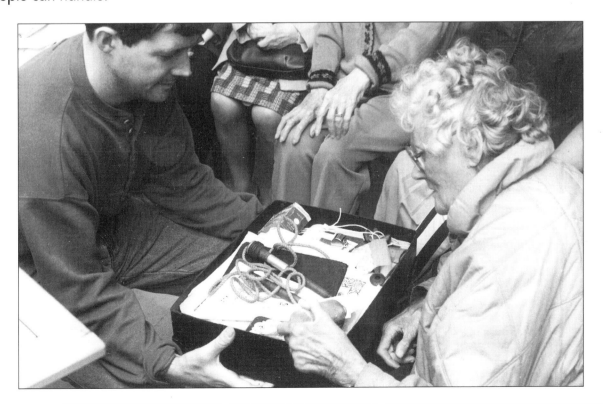

There are various ways of using objects:

A.   Make a collection of objects relevant to the theme to be handled, demonstrated, and discussed.

B.   Place objects within view in the centre of the group like a still life.

C.   A good way of beginning a session is to ask people to choose something from a collection of relevant objects handed round on a tray or open basket and talk about the memories the object brings to mind.

D.   A different version of **C.** is to ask people to feel and identify or choose an object unseen in a closed bag as a preliminary to talking about memories. They can be asked to guess what the object is before pulling it out and checking if they were right.

6. MAKING A LIST

A surprisingly successful reminiscence activity is for group members to make a list of everything they remember connected with a particular theme or topic. Have a large sheet of paper and write things down as they are mentioned in large writing. This activity can be a preliminary for discussing items on the list in more detail later, or people may want to discuss things as they remember them.

For example: ask people as a group to remember all the games which they used to play as children, write the games down on a large sheet of paper, permit only a little discussion as it occurs, but focus mainly on remembering more games. You can go back and discuss in more detail later.

Other good listing topics: fabrics and what they were used for, things sold in a grocer's shop, household tasks, contents of a school satchel.

7. MAPS

Local, regional, world maps are a useful focus for reminiscence sessions. Plot where people have lived and travelled to. On local maps you can identify changes in local geography.

People can also draw their own personal maps showing their birth place, or somewhere important to them in the centre of the paper, and the rest of the world they have experienced radiating out from the centre.

8. MUSIC AND SOUNDS

Music is very evocative and can be useful in reminiscence to prompt memories, to provide a group activity, and to stimulate a part of the memory that is different from the sentence-making part.

It is a good idea to develop a collection of tapes for reminiscence purposes. Use reminiscence sessions to discover the full range of the musical tastes and experiences of the group members. See what people's reactions are to many different forms of recorded and live music from brass bands to dance band music, try also opera, musicals, folk songs and dances, national music, classical, ballet music, jazz, popular songs, choral singing.

A.   Music relevant to the theme can be sung, played on tapes or performed as live music. Music relevant to the theme can be music about the theme or music which someone remembers and associates with an occasion. For instance for a session on courting, relevant music would be songs about love or a particular piece of music which someone remembers from that time.

B.   Recorded sounds can be useful. Tapes are available commercially from various companies including the BBC and can sometimes be borrowed from libraries. Examples are a steam train or seagulls to set a scene or trigger memories, or the voices of famous people, such as politicians, royalty or entertainers. The group can of course make their own sounds to go with a particular scene or topic.

9. OUTINGS

An outing is a good way of varying reminiscence activities, particularly for people who do not get out much. Use the outing to discuss what can be seen around you or to prompt memories of the past.

A.   Go out to the sorts of places discussed in reminiscence: tea shops, fish and chip shops, markets, cinema, the seaside.

B.   Go back to places known in the past; streets, schools, parks, houses.

C.   Local history museums often display everyday objects familiar to older people, and may have domestic room settings.

Some museums have handling collections which the group may enjoy more than just looking. The museum staff may be interested in hearing about the memories of members of the group.

10. PRACTICAL ACTIVITIES

A.   Doing everyday tasks not usually done by members of the group any longer, such as hand washing or polishing, can be good reminiscence activities particularly for people who cannot use speech very much. Others may enjoy practical activities too.

B.   Many people enjoy being involved in cooking, especially if they no longer normally do this for themselves. Get people doing familiar movements such as breaking eggs, peeling potatoes, stirring, and kneading.

Another approach is to involve people in giving instructions about how to cook old recipes while you do the actual cooking and then serve the results to them.

C.   Involve people in other practical activities which were a familiar part of their life in the past. Ideas include gardening, carpentry, sewing, looking after animals.

11. PROMPTED REMINISCENCE

Encouraging people to describe their memories in response to questions is the most common form of reminiscence. The leader in this form of reminiscence activity should develop skill in asking questions which will stimulate memories and not make people feel a failure if they cannot answer. See the section on **WAYS OF ASKING QUESTIONS**.

It is helpful to develop some knowledge of the subjects being discussed by reading oral and social history publications and by talking to people so that you can provide appropriate prompts. As well as knowledge, it is useful to develop a skill in identifying clues to fruitful areas to explore.

In the **IDEAS SECTIONS,** you will find questions or topics to use for prompted reminiscence. Make a note for yourself of other prompts which you find useful.

12. READ A QUOTATION

Several of the **IDEAS SECTIONS** include an excerpt from a published source. Reading something aloud, a personal memory from an oral history book or an official document, is sometimes a good way of focusing on a theme and prompting agreement, disagreement and further discussion.

13. SHOWING AROUND

Memories about places are stimulated by visualising the place and even by imagining that you are showing someone round. Get someone to remember their kitchen/home/street etc by asking them to describe it to someone as if they were showing them round. Being able to move is useful but not essential here. Group members and the person being shown round should be encouraged to prompt and ask questions.

14. STORY TELLING

Using memories to tell a story makes a change from remembering facts. Several times in the **IDEAS SECTIONS** I have suggested that you set things going by providing a starting point for a story to be continued by members of the group. This works well as a communal activity with people either taking turns or contributing as they think of something to say. Encourage people to contribute ideas about the sort of things which they remember happening. If the story goes well, write it down and read it out at the end.

15. THEN AND NOW

There are many ways of relating memories of the past to the present and doing so is often a useful way of ending a session.

A.   One way of doing this is to relate something remembered in the past to something in the present.
    EXAMPLE: leader: *'Mabel remembered that her first dance dress was pink satin and today she is wearing a pink cardigan'.*

B.   Another way is to describe or ask someone to describe a modern version of an old object.
    EXAMPLE: *'Here is a flat iron which had to be heated on a stove; today we have electric irons'.*

Alternatively have two objects which fulfil the same function and discuss the advantages and disadvantages of each.

C. Modern pictures can be used to discuss differences and similarities between the past and the present. Make a collection of pictures, perhaps cut from magazines, to use. Shop interiors, school classrooms, clothes, domestic and office equipment, and people at work are good subjects.

16. THINGS LEARNED BY HEART

The memory of things learned by heart lasts longer than the ability to generate speech, so it is good to make opportunities for people to use things they have learned in this way. Encourage people to say poems, monologues, rhymes, counting out songs, mnemonics, catch phrases, slogans, prayers and to sing songs relevant to the theme.

17. TASTE, TOUCH AND SMELL

Things which people can touch, taste or smell are good as an added dimension for any group. Make a collection of suitable objects, for example: foods, spices, fabrics, natural objects, medicinal smells such as camphorated oil, household cleaning materials, things with a special cultural significance. Get people to touch, smell or taste the objects as appropriate and ask them about the memories which are prompted.

The use of touch, taste and smell can be a particularly appropriate way of working with people who do not respond to speech very much on account of mental frailty. For instance, in Autumn, collect some chestnuts in their prickly cases. Give someone a chestnut to hold and point out to them how smooth and brown and shiny it is. Show them how the chestnut fits into its prickly case, how soft the inside of the case is and how prickly the outside is. Say something about children gathering chestnuts in the autumn. Have two chestnuts threaded on strings and see if the person will swing one of them.

18. USING PICTURES

Well chosen reminiscence pictures, illustrated books, maps, pictures of the local area, postcards, old magazines can be very useful triggers. Use them selectively and be prepared to find that some people will have difficulty seeing them. People's own old photographs are also an excellent reminiscence aid.

1. HOME LIFE

If you are not sure how far the group members want to talk about highly personal things, start by focusing on more impersonal memories like rooms and activities at home or food.

You will soon get a sense of whether people want to talk about their parents and brothers and sisters in a more personal way.

Be very conscious that not everyone was brought up with two parents and brothers and sisters.

People will have lived in smaller or larger family groupings, possibly involving adults other than parents.

Some people living in residential care in their old age, may well have lived in residential homes when they were children.

WHERE WAS HOME TO YOU?

ASKING ROUND THE GROUP/ A STARTING ACTIVITY

In order to start to establish a little information about people's background, ask if everyone can say where they think of when asked *'Where was home to you as a child?'* Then go on to a question such as *'Who was part of your home?'*

FAMILY PHOTOGRAPHS

USING PICTURES/ A STARTING ACTIVITY

Encourage people to bring to the session some old family photographs to show the others.

Some people will need help in remembering to bring them or finding them, so the support of a carer could be useful.

BATH NIGHT

READ A QUOTATION/ A STARTING ACTIVITY

Read out this memory to start people talking about whether it is similar or different from their experience.

❝Friday night was bath night. My Mum had five boys and two girls. We all had to share the same water. There'd be a couple of us in it at one time. We'd have a right old scrub with Lifebuoy soap. I remember her doing our ears. To keep the water warm you had to continually top up the bath with a bucket of hot water and scoop out the cold.❞

MY FAMILY

MAKING A FAMILY TREE

One way of remembering home life is get everyone to draw up a family tree. Start with the parents and then name the children. Help people who need assistance.
Use this activity to enable people to talk about family relationships and feelings if they want to.
If people respond positively to making an outline family tree, you can encourage them to elaborate it by adding drawn portraits or photocopied pictures of members of the family with a written memory about each of them.

A LIFE STORY BOOK

WRITING ACTIVITY

A family tree could be the start of a Life Story Book - a scrapbook made by or with someone which tells the story of their life and reminds them or others about their life events.

MY FAMILY TREE

Enlarge this family tree to A3 size on a photocopier and use as a teaching resource.

AN IMAGINARY FAMILY PHOTO

A DRAMA IDEA

Help someone make an imaginary 'family photograph' by asking them to pose other members of the group as if they were that person's family.

Let the person concerned tell each group member who they represent, how they should sit, what they would have been wearing, what the expression on their face would be and what they might say.

If you can take an instant photograph with a Polaroid camera the activity will be all the more memorable.

Repeat this for several members of the group.

MY HOME

SHOWING ROUND

Ask a member of the group to 'show someone round' their childhood home. Get the person to move around in their memory starting with the front door, explaining where the rooms were in relation to the entrance, what furniture there was in each room, going upstairs if there were rooms upstairs, and saying which people or activities they associate with which room.

Encourage people to remember smells, tastes and textures associated with different rooms.

The process of explaining and moving helps the memory process particularly vividly.

MY HOME

DRAWING

Another way of prompting memories of home is by asking people to draw a rough ground plan of the rooms and noting down what went on in each room - both the furniture and decorations and which family members were usually found where, (for example 'mother was usually in the kitchen'). You can extend this to include the outside - the garden, yard or common parts of a block of flats.

Extend the plan if you wish to outside the home to include the land around and what went on there.

Get the members of the group to do this themselves if they can. If they cannot, do the drawing for them either individually or as a group, asking for suggestions about what to draw and prompting if necessary.

MOTHER'S SAYINGS

MAKING A LIST

Ask the group to remember all the things their mother or father used to say to them routinely about behaving properly and list them down on a large sheet of paper.

SOME SUGGESTIONS:

• have you washed behind your ears ? • eat up your first course if you want any afters •

• take a clean handkerchief • remember your ps and qs (pleases and thank yous) •

FAMILY MEALTIMES

PROMPTED REMINISCENCE

Meal time rituals and habits are often interesting for people to recall.

PROMPTS:

- Where did your family eat meals?
- Who was usually there at meal times?
- Did people have particular places around the table?
- Do you remember the china or utensils?
- Who did the cooking, serving, clearing and washing up?

- Were there prayers to start or finish?
- Which people talked a great deal or very little?
- What were typical conversation topics?
- Were the children reminded about table manners or other family rules (such as finishing up their cabbage)?
- Did anyone get preferential treatment if there were special titbits or shortages?

FAMILY MEALTIMES

A DRAMA IDEA

Use ideas from the previous discussion on which to base a drama activity. One possibility would be to get all, or some of, the group members sitting around a table. Suggest that they are a family having a meal together. Encourage them to choose roles for themselves, or choose roles for them, and get them talking.

POSSIBLE ROLES: a busy mother, grandmother, father, two or three children.

They could decide what to say themselves or look to other members of the group for ideas.

FOOD

PROMPTED REMINISCENCE/MAKING A LIST

Remembering the food of childhood is often an enjoyable experience and can lead to other interesting discussions and activities.

You could start by asking people if there is any food they particularly remember or anything which was their childhood favourite.

Go on perhaps by getting people to list all the dishes remembered from childhood, particularly things that they do not have often nowadays. Prompts such as brawn, bread and dripping, pease-pudding and faggots, bubble and squeak will probably start off an English group. People brought up in the Caribbean may remember snapper fish, sugar cane, calaloo, plantain. Encourage people to remember the food of their childhood whatever part of the world they grew up in.

See if particular foods were associated with different days of the week.

DIFFERENT NAMES FOR FOOD

HANDLING OBJECTS

If members of the group spent their childhood in different parts of the world or in different parts of the British Isles, you could find out what they called various fruit, vegetables or cooked dishes when they were young.

With a multicultural group, bring examples of fruit or vegetables which are eaten in many parts of the world to the session. Aubergines, bananas, onions, green beans and rice would be suitable. Ask people what they called these things in their mother tongue or their dialect. Go on to discuss how the food was cooked and prepared in different places.

Go on to discover the names for other food stuffs.

A similar activity focused around bread, cakes, buns would probably produce a variety of names from group members who were all of British origin.

THE FOOD WE HAD AT HOME

TOUCH, TASTE AND SMELL

People who no longer cook for themselves may not have handled uncooked vegetables or meat for some time. A bag of unwashed potatoes, a bunch of carrots with the tops on, and even a pound of sausages or shoulder of lamb will be reminiscence triggers. Many shops also now stock food stuffs from all over the world. Bring in some exotic fruit and non-European vegetables or fish if such items are part of people's experience.

People without much speech can be encouraged to feel and smell the food stuffs and peel or chop the vegetables.

WHAT WE WOULD LIKE TO EAT NOW

THEN AND NOW

If the group is meeting in a place where meals are provided, you could use the reminiscence about food to discuss whether there are things which members of the group would like to have cooked for them now.

If there are, perhaps who ever cooks for them could discuss their ideas and suggestions and see if such things could be included on the menu on a regular or occasional basis.

RECIPES   WRITING

Discussion about food could also lead to people remembering or researching recipes to make a collection of recipes. Perhaps they could even make a booklet to be given or sold to others. Try gathering the recipes under such headings as: old favourites, special dishes or war time economy cooking.

COOKING   PRACTICAL ACTIVITY/TASTE, TOUCH & SMELL

Perhaps the group could do some cooking. Try to make things which have been mentioned in reminiscence. Encourage people who are very mentally frail to do the familiar actions of stirring, chopping, whisking, spooning, washing. Let them taste, smell and feel the cooking ingredients. Talk about the food, the cooking equipment and the cooking methods. You may need to tell yourself that their involvement in the process is more important than having a good end-product.

SOMETHING TO TASTE   AN OUTING

If group members have enjoyed discussing food see if you can locate any shops or cafes within visiting distance to eat or take away such traditional foods as jellied eels, pie and mash, fish and chips, Asian sweets or food, Caribbean cooking.

GARDENING   PRACTICAL ACTIVITY/TASTE, TOUCH & SMELL

Gardening is another practical activity which in the past some people would have been involved in. Planting bulbs, sowing seeds, planting annuals and growing vegetables and herbs are possible projects if there is a garden or if you have some large tubs.
Consult people in deciding what to grow as well as involving them in the physical work if they can do it.
If some of the group are interested, see if you can arrange a visit to a garden centre, to nearby allotments, to a local horticultural show, or to the park.

THINGS WERE STRICTER THEN   THEN AND NOW

Some older people think that children have rather an easy time of it now. It is worth encouraging a discussion about this sort of statement. See if you can discover the range of things that people were allowed to do or not allowed to do when they were children. Within a group there is likely to be considerable difference.

Compared with today there will be some areas of greater restriction and others of greater freedom. For instance girls may not have been allowed out as late as now, but children may have had greater freedom in the past to play outside and explore when there was so much less traffic.

THEN AND NOW

OLDER PEOPLE & GRANDPARENTS

Start by asking what they remember from their childhood about their grandparents or other older people. Go on to a discussion of how things differ now from then. Probe a little if people have an idealised picture of the past being much better for all older people. Ask about what pensions, medical care, home support, housing was available for older people when they were young.

MUSIC/FINISHING ACTIVITY

SWEETS

Ask for suggestions of a song remembered from childhood to end with. Encourage people to remember something their mother, father or a grandparent used to sing.

TOUCH, TASTE & SMELL/FINISHING ACTIVITY

SWEETS

Hand round a selection of traditional sweets which can still be bought loose from some sweet shops. Some suggestions are : liquorice, pear drops, aniseed balls, gob stoppers, bulls eyes, barley sugar, treacle toffee, sherbet fountains.
Then ask everyone in turn what their favourite sort of sweet was when they were children.

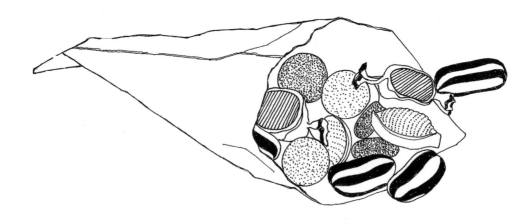

2. HOUSEWORK

Reminiscence about housework tasks frequently prompts vivid memories about domestic tasks no longer undertaken and considerable pride in a high level of skill. The topic provides an opportunity for discussion about hard work, about differences between then and now, about the changing roles of men and women, and the responsibilities of children in helping in the home.

One of the major domestic tasks, which has perhaps changed more than many others, is washing. Before the use of washing machines and the provision as a matter of course of constant running hot water, doing the family's washing took at least a day.

Remember to include the memories of people whose experiences are different from those dominant in the group either because they were much richer or much poorer or because they grew up in a different culture.

HOUSEWORK — MAKING A LIST/STARTING ACTIVITY

Ask people to 'brainstorm' all the housework activities which were undertaken in their childhood. Once the activities have been remembered, you can ask for detailed information about the equipment used, how the work was done, and who did it.

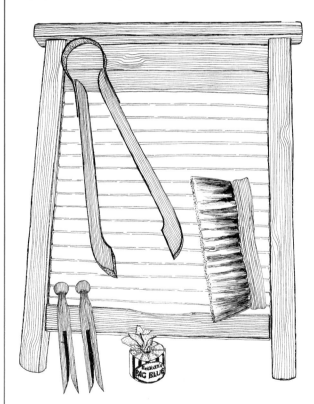

SOME PROMPTS:

- fetching water
- washing clothes
- sweeping and scrubbing the floor and ground outside
- beating the carpets
- fetching wood and coal
- laying, lighting, maintaining and cleaning the fire
- polishing ornaments, furniture, the fender
- cleaning the knives
- mending shoes
- turning the beds
- cutting up newspaper for toilet paper
- cooking

CLEANING UTENSILS — HANDLING OBJECTS/STARTING ACTIVITY

Bring to the group a collection of household cleaning utensils and materials for people to handle. Many of them have changed little over the years and can be found around the house, or bought from old fashioned hardware shops or junk shops.

SUGGESTIONS : wooden scrubbing brush, hand brush, yellow duster, piece of pumice stone, tin of brasso, lavender polish, polishing cloths, some lumps of coal, a bundle of kindling wood, blue bag for the washing, wooden clothes pegs, washboard, wooden washing tongs.

As people handle the objects encourage them to discuss how they were used, what they were for and what else was involved in the tasks they were used for.

GUESS THE MIME

DRAMA IDEA/STARTING ACTIVITY

Mime a housework activity such as sweeping or scrubbing and see if people can guess what it is you are doing.

Turn this into a game by asking everyone in turn to mime something for the others to guess. You could make it more challenging by saying that no one can repeat the same activity as someone else.

Help people if they need it by showing them such mimes as: wringing out wet washing, turning the handle of a mangle, ironing, polishing, spitting on shoes while cleaning them, chopping up fire wood, fetching water, lighting a fire.

WASHDAY

PROMPTED REMINISCENCE

Focus on wash day and encourage people to remember as much detail as possible.

- On which days of the week were the wash day tasks done?
- At what time did work begin?
- Was there running water and if not how was water fetched?
- How was the water heated?
- What sort of soap or detergent was used?
- How was the wash rinsed, bleached, starched?
- How was the washing dried?
- How was the ironing done? What sorts of irons were used?
- How were they heated?
- How often was clothing and bedding changed?
- What other ways were there of getting washing done: sending it out, having someone in to do it?

WASHDAY
DRAMA IDEA

With a few props and some pretence, you, or some of the group members, could act out all the wash day tasks. Ask for help and instructions from the group. Ask for detailed information about how to do things.

Bring characters into this drawn from people's memories; for instance the harassed mother, the child who wants to go out but has to stay in to help, the sick child watching the work, neighbours chatting as they wash or hang things out on the line.

WHO DID WHAT?
PROMPTED REMINISCENCE

Prompt a discussion about whose job the various household tasks were. This will enable people to focus on the differences between households as well as the similarities.
Some people may have grown up with paid household help, others may have been themselves paid to do housework.

Raise the question of the responsibilities of children to work and what they as children felt about their chores if they had them.

Take the opportunity to discuss the role of men and boys in relation to housework in the past and now.

USING THE OBJECTS
PRACTICAL ACTIVITY

Even without using much speech, people can become involved with remembering the movements associated with household objects.

For instance give someone a piece of cloth and a washboard and encourage them to show you how the cloth was rubbed on the board. Similarly ask to be shown how a flat iron was heated and how its temperature tested.

You can make the situation more real.

- Get people to help you with hand washing. If you cannot take them to a sink, bring a bowl of warm, soapy, bubbly water to them and something to wash. Encourage them to feel the water, dip the washing in and out, rub and wring it.

- Have some sheets or linen and ask people to help you with the folding. Stand opposite some one each holding one corner of a sheet, for example, shake it out and then fold it progressively.

- Have some brass ornaments which need polishing, some cloths and a tin of brasso, so people can do some polishing.

- Think of other household tasks which people might do: dusting, polishing furniture, cleaning shoes.

USING THE SENSES

TOUCH AND SMELL

■ **SMELL:**

encourage people to smell scented soap, household soap, brass polish, furniture polish.

■ **FEEL:**

ask people to feel the heavy weight of a flat iron, the roughness of a wash board, warm bubbly water, a hard prickly scrubbing brush.

IMAGINE THE SMELL

PROMPTED REMINISCENCE

It is possible to remember smells purely by an act of imagination. Mention a characteristic smell associated with housework and see if people can conjure it up in their imagination.

Suitable examples are: the smell of hot, soapy washing or a freshly polished floor. See if anyone has a smell they want to remember.

I"LL SHOW YOU THE KITCHEN

SHOWING ROUND

Ask someone to describe their memories of the kitchen, scullery or wash house as if they were there and they were showing someone round. The memories will be stimulated if they can move around or at least turn one way or the other. Help them with prompts.

Suggest that they describe the room, the furniture, the cupboards and point out all the things needed for doing housework tasks. Encourage them to include the people they would expect to see in the room and describe what they are doing.

THE KITCHEN

DRAWING

Ask people to draw, or draw for them to their description, the kitchen or place where the cooking was done. Include the facilities for cooking, washing up, food preparation and storage and eating.

An alternative is to make a drawing about where people did their washing. Include if appropriate the sink, the copper, the fuel, the mangle, indoor and outdoor drying lines, bowls or baskets, ironing arrangements.

SPRING CLEANING

A DRAMA IDEA

or PREPARING FOR A SPECIAL HOLIDAY

Many people will have memories of times of extra-thorough cleaning and housework either once a year in spring or in preparation for a special day (a wedding perhaps) or at a particular time of year (for a religious festival).

Ask people to describe all the things that had to be done and what the household atmosphere was like. If this seems a fruitful area of reminiscence, see if it would lend itself to a role play, perhaps of members of a household getting cross with each other or of people happily co-operating to get the work done.

DOMESTIC INTERIORS

OUTING

Local history museums often display domestic interiors with household equipment. Some stately homes do too, particularly if the kitchen or servants' quarters are on view.

See if you can locate a suitable place to visit and take a group to. Normally objects in such places cannot be touched, but some places have a handling collection and it would be worth enquiring in advance about whether one exists in the place you plan to go to.

MAKING AND MENDING

PROMPTED REMINISCENCE/PRACTICAL ACTIVITY

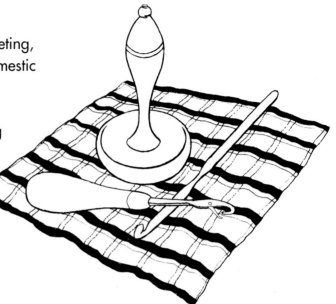

Sewing, darning and mending, knitting, crocheting, tatting and rug-making may be among the domestic activities which people remember.

See if you can borrow or acquire items of the equipment people used, for instance a darning egg or mushroom, crochet and rug making hooks, to start off a discussion.

Arrange for people to have a go at some individual handwork such as knitting, or plan and make a group embroidery or rug.

TALKING ABOUT THE PRESENT

THEN AND NOW

Refer to some of the things the group has remembered and then go on to ask them how housework is done today. Some things have changed considerably, others have remained much the same.

See if they can remember when they first used electrical household machines such as a vacuum cleaner, a washing machine, electric irons, gas or electric stoves.

IT WAS ON A MONDAY MORNING

MUSIC/FINISHING ACTIVITY

If the song *'It was on a Monday morning that I beheld my darling'*, also known as *'Dashing away with the smoothing iron'*, is familiar to you and members of the group it is good one to sing to end a session on washing because it goes through all the wash day activities. The actions can be mimed by the group.

3. CHILDREN AT PLAY

Many people really enjoy remembering the games they used to play as children and many games are played, with variations, all over the world. Children at play is a topic which will highlight the similarities and differences of experience of people brought up in different places.

A session on playing is often a chance for people to laugh and be silly. Some people or groups will be unwilling to risk their dignity, others will really welcome the chance to unbend. Reminiscence about childhood games is an excellent opportunity for joining up with a group of children.

You may find that some people had few opportunities to play in any real sense because they had to help with adult tasks from a young age. Acknowledge their experience too.

HAND ROUND SOME TOYS   HANDLING OBJECTS/A STARTING ACTIVITY

Have available some traditional toys such as a skipping rope, a rubber ball, some white chalk, a rag doll, conkers threaded on strings, a wooden yoyo, some marbles, and some jacks.

Ask people to take an object and talk about the memories it brings back.

HOPSCOTCH or SKIPPING

PRACTICAL ACTIVITY/ A STARTING ACTIVITY

Without saying anything at first, draw a hop scotch on the floor with chalk and hop up and down the grid.

Alternatively, use a skipping rope to skip for a few minutes. Then ask people what memories of childhood games are prompted.

Encourage them to try the hop scotch or skipping rope themselves.

PLAYING THE GAMES

HANDLING OBJECTS

If you have objects available, ask people to show you how the toys were played with. As people show you, encourage them to remember more and more detail about the rules and methods of the game and where and with whom the games were played.

Even if people can no longer do the actions as well as they used to, encourage them to have a go at skipping, rolling a marble across the floor, flicking a playing card, hopping or walking round a hop scotch grid, turning a long rope for others.

There will be many different ways of playing traditional games. Hop scotch for instance is drawn out in many ways. Encourage people to talk about or demonstrate their own way and compare with other people's versions.

SKIPPING RHYMES

THINGS LEARNED BY HEART

Skipping is associated with many rhymes. If you start people off with one of the rhymes printed here, they may be able to remember the words and perhaps recite several more. A long rope held by two people across the group and turned rhythmically may help. Discuss the different sorts of skipping which people did and the rhymes which accompanied them: skipping alone, skipping in pairs, skipping with a group.

Write the rhymes down and compare them with rhymes sung by children today. Many of them will be similar.

Ask people whose childhood language is not English if they can remember and recite the skipping songs they know.

SOME TRADITIONAL SKIPPING RHYMES:

'Salt, mustard, vinegar pepper
Salt, mustard, vinegar pepper'

'Blackcurrant, redcurrant, raspberry tart,
Tell me the name of your sweetheart,
A,B,C,D,E etc'

'All in together girls,
Never mind the weather girls,
When I call your birthday
Please run out
January, February, March etc'

A CARIBBEAN SKIPPING RHYME:

'Mosquito one, mosquito two
Mosquito jump in the hot calaloo'

OTHER RHYMES & SONGS   THINGS LEARNED BY HEART

As well as skipping games, there are many other rhymes and songs which are associated with playing games in childhood particularly counting out rhymes and singing games. See whether members of the group can remember any.

An example of a counting out rhyme is 'one potato, two potato etc'. Singing games are such games as 'Ring a ring a roses', 'Fair Jenny lies a weeping' and 'Oranges and lemons'.

PLAYING WITH A DOLL   TOUCHING

Give people a doll to examine. Encourage them to rock or pat the doll, undress it, wrap it up in a blanket. Talk to them while they handle the doll.

This is a good activity for people who do not speak much.

You can encourage people who are more verbal to remember their own favourite doll or cuddly toy, to describe it, and describe how they got it.

NAME THE DOLL   ASKING ROUND THE GROUP

After they have had a chance to examine the doll, hand the doll to each person in turn and ask them to say what they would call it if it were theirs. People with very little speech may be able to contribute a one word name.

MAKING A LIST OF GAMES   MAKING A LIST

On some large sheets of paper write down the name of as many games as people can remember. They may well be surprised by how many they can list. You can help them by thinking of games you played as a child and the games played by children you know.

Encourage people to remember the names of national or regional games, variations and versions.

Once you have made a list, or as you do so, you could discuss whether games were winter or summer games, whether they took place inside or outside, whether they were played by girls or boys, and whether they think children still play such games today.

BOARD GAMES PROMPTED REMINISCENCE/PRACTICAL ACTIVITY

Start by encouraging people to remember the board games they used to play - ludo, snakes and ladders, Chinese checkers, alma, shove ha'penny, dominoes. See if anyone remembers other board games, particularly games from other parts of the world such as 'wari' which is played in Africa, Asia and the Caribbean; 'pachesi', played in India; the Chinese game of 'Go'.

The group might then decide to have a game playing session. Much of the equipment will be easily available.

If you and the group become enthusiastic, there is a fascinating book published by UNICEF called *"Games of the World"* by Frederic Grunfeld which describes many traditional games, details how they are played and shows how the necessary equipment can be simply made. The library may have a copy of the book.

PLAYING CARDS   PROMPTED REMINISCENCE

Ask people if they enjoyed playing cards and what games they used to play. Talk about the games and prompt memories of when people used to play them and with whom; for instance on train journeys, in secret dens, round a camp fire.

If people are interested, arrange a card game session.

RELATIONSHIPS   PROMPTED REMINISCENCE

Talking about play can provide an opportunity to discuss the social context of play and what they felt about it. People have many memories about friendships between children - best friends, quarrels, gangs. Playing in single or mixed sex groups is often a good discussion topic.

Other ideas are: playing with brothers or sisters, rules imposed by parents, rules imposed by children, other people's parents.

HOMEMADE TOYS   PROMPTED REMINISCENCE/ PRACTICAL ACTIVITIES

Many people made their own toys - dolls from clothes pegs or rags, skipping ropes woven from parcel string, small carts and carts big enough to sit in from wood, kites from tissue paper and split bamboo. They may have also made games from natural objects such as sticks, stones, chestnuts or from household things such as borrowed plates, cotton reels, buttons.

Discuss what people made and how they played with the toys. Then, if the group members wish, assemble the materials to have a making session following the instructions they give you.

CREATING A SCENE

DRAMA IDEAS

If the group members enjoy acting, you might be able to identify in the previous discussion the seeds of an enjoyable few minutes of drama perhaps involving quarrelling children or cross parents.

Encourage some of the group members to act out a scene someone has described, or speak it out if moving about is not appropriate, and get the others to provide prompts.

REMINISCENCE WITH CHILDREN

CROSS-GENERATIONAL ACTIVITY

Arrange for a small group of children (maybe from a local school or a group of grandchildren) to join the reminiscence group for a joint session on childhood games. Such an exchange is an excellent bridge between the generations. It enables the older people to tell the children about what they used to play and perhaps also show them. Both groups, young and old, may be able to explore the similarities and differences between children now and in the past.

Making toys together as described in the previous activity might be a good joint activity.

WATCHING CHILDREN AT PLAY

OUTING/THEN AND NOW

Arrange to take the reminiscence group to watch children at play, perhaps in a school play ground or park. Discuss the similarities and differences between what the children are observed doing and how the older people remember playing.

MAKE UP A STORY ABOUT CHILDREN

STORYTELLING

Start with something like this,

'One day 60 years ago two sisters were out in the street near their house with nothing to do.

Along came their friend from next door with a length of rope'.

Ask people to suggest what happened next and ask each person in turn to add an idea or sentence to the story.

Write the story down if the idea catches on.

MYSELF AS A CHILD

ASKING ROUND THE GROUP/ FINISHING ACTIVITY

Suggest that people try to remember themselves as a child playing outside or inside and then ask them to describe briefly what they were playing, what they were wearing, who they were with.

MY FAVOURITE GAME

ASKING ROUND THE GROUP/ THEN AND NOW/FINISHING ACTIVITY

Go round the group asking them to say what they have particularly enjoyed remembering, *'I have enjoyed remembering how I used to play....'*.

You could bring the members into the present by adding a further statement about what they like to do nowadays, *'Nowadays I like to .....'*

CHILDHOOD SONGS

MUSIC/FINISHING ACTIVITY

Ask for suggestions of a song which people remember from their childhood and sing it together.

4. SCHOOL DAYS

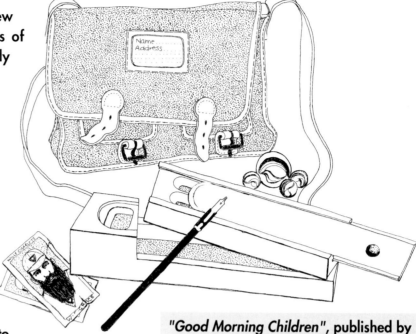

School attendance is one of the few experiences which all members of any reminiscence group are likely to have had.

Nevertheless people's memories of their school are bound to be very different as well as having many similarities.

Some people still have painful memories of harsh treatment; others will enjoy laughing at things they used to do.

You can use this session to celebrate skills which people still have, for instance the ability to recite poems, remember the times tables, add pounds, shillings and pence or write with fine handwriting.

"Good Morning Children", published by Age Exchange, is a useful source of memories about school days and pictures of children.

SING A SONG
MUSIC/STARTING ACTIVITY

Many people who went to school in Britain and elsewhere learnt the hymn 'All Things Bright and Beautiful' at school. You could start or end the session by asking people to remember and sing the hymn or play a tape of it. Other frequently remembered hymns are 'Jesus bids us shine with a kindly light' and 'Jesus wants me for a sunbeam' or in autumn 'We plough the fields and scatter the good seed on the land'.

WHERE I WENT TO SCHOOL
ASKING AROUND THE GROUP/STARTING ACTIVITY

Ask each member of the group the name of the school or schools they went to and where it was. Write the replies up on a board or large sheet of paper where everyone can see it.

THINGS TO HANDLE
HANDLING OBJECTS/ STARTING ACTIVITY

Assemble a collection of new or old objects associated with school, for instance a traditional satchel, wooden pencil box, exercise book, wooden ruler, a dip pen. Include some marbles or cigarette cards too.

Examine the objects with the group members and ask them what memories the objects prompt.

WHAT MY SCHOOL DAYS WERE LIKE

PROMPTED REMINISCENCE

Encourage general memories of school days with such prompts as:

- Describe what your school looked like outside.
  (Remember: some people may have had lessons in the open air)
- Describe what sort of furniture there was in a classroom.

  Was there a school hall and what was it like?

  What subjects did people learn?

  Which were your favourite lessons?

  When did school start?

  When did it finish?

  Was any food provided?

  Was there any time to play? If so what do you remember playing and where?

- Describe some of the teachers.

WHAT WOULD YOU HAVE HAD IN YOUR SATCHEL?

ASKING AROUND THE GROUP

Ask everyone in turn to say one item which they might have taken to school in their satchel or bag.

Prompts: • a sandwich • a penny for some sweets • a pen and pencil • a pencil box, • a comic • cigarette cards • a piece of toffee • a mouse.

You could encourage any jokers in the group to say unlikely things to make people laugh.

See if people can, with help, recite what everyone else has said before adding their own item on the lines of the game *'I went to market yesterday and I bought...'*. Start off with *'I looked in my satchel and I found...'*

FAVOURITE TEACHERS

ASKING AROUND THE GROUP

Ask everyone in turn to describe their favourite teacher. Go round the group a second time asking for descriptions of their least favourite teacher.

GETTING INTO TROUBLE

A DRAMA IDEA

Discussions about misbehaving at school, getting into trouble, and being punished lead very easily into a few minutes of acting. Start things off yourself by pretending to be a strict teacher telling someone off for cheating, being late, or talking. Then encourage someone to reply in the role of a defiant or contrite pupil. Ask members of the group what the strict teacher would have said and how the pupil in trouble would have replied.

If people have particular memories of getting into trouble, they may enjoy acting with others their own particular situation.

POEMS, SONGS AND RHYMES

PROMPTED REMINISCENCE

Poems, songs and rhymes learnt by heart are well remembered even by people with other forms of memory loss.

Ask if anyone can remember a poem they learned at school to recite to the group. If they get stuck offer to look out a copy of the poem for another time. Palgrave's *"Golden Treasury of Verse"* was a traditional source of school poetry and is still available.

Try starting people off with the two times table (once two is two, two twos are four, etc) and see how they go. They may be pleased to recite other multiplication tables and may do it better than you.

POUNDS, SHILLINGS AND PENCE

PRACTICAL ACTIVITY

If you are under about 30, you probably hardly remember pre-decimal coins. In that case, ask the group to set you some sums involving pounds, shillings and pence, then show you how to do them.

BEST HAND WRITING

PRACTICAL ACTIVITY

Discuss what sort of hand writing people learned at school and how they were taught. Provide a pencil and paper for anyone who wishes to show off their best hand writing. Some people may still be able to do the curly hand known as 'copper plate' and would enjoy trying to do it again using pen and ink. Provide them with a dip pen, a bottle of ink, some paper and a blotter.

Ask people who can write in different scripts to do some writing and perhaps teach the group how to write something.

CLASSROOMS THEN

PROMPTED REMINISCENCE

Ask several people to describe in detail their classroom: what furniture there was and how it was arranged, where the teacher sat, how the room was heated, what was on the walls. Draw individual pictures or a group picture of a classroom.

CLASSROOMS NOW

OUTING/THEN & NOW

Try to arrange a visit to a modern school to make comparisons A local school might be interested in using the memories of the reminiscence group for school project work, and the group members may well be interested in seeing a modern school and in being used as an authority about schooling in the past.

SCHOOL CLOTHES

USING PICTURES/DRAWING ACTIVITY

Collect some photographs of school children, contemporary and from the past.
Use these to prompt memories of what people wore to school. It might have been a uniform or their own clothes with a special overall or pinafore.

Continue this theme by asking them to draw themselves as youngsters in their school clothes, or draw for them following their descriptions if they cannot do a drawing themselves.

If this goes well, you could make a group picture or collage using people's individual pictures showing everyone as schoolchildren sitting in a classroom.

MY OLD SCHOOL

MAPS

If you are working with a group who are still living in the area where they were brought up, you could mark on a map where people lived, where they went to school, and what their route to school was.

You could plan a trip to visit people's old school if it is still there and see how it has changed.

SPECIAL OCCASIONS

PROMPTED REMINISCENCE

Empire Day, 25th May, was a big school festival in Britain and in many parts of the former Empire. People may have memories of parades in the school playground, special clothes, plays, tableaux and a half day holiday.

Find out about other special school occasions, such as, May Day, Harvest Festival, St Patrick's Day, Christmas, the Jubilee of King George V and Queen Mary in 1935, other national holidays, Prize Day, or the day the school photographer came.

EXTRA WORK   PROMPTED REMINISCENCE

For some people their school days were particularly hard because they had to work as well , maybe helping at home before and after school or in the dinner break. Encourage people to talk about this sort of work or outside tasks in the fields

CHANGING SCHOOLS   THEN AND NOW

Memories of starting at a new school are often vivid and sometimes unhappy, but people may be interested in discussing them and comparing notes.

You might also want to go from reminiscence to using remembered feelings about coping with change to help people deal with a current situation. For instance if there are changes taking place at the setting where people are meeting - for instance staff changes, a new older person coming, changes to the building.

LEAVING SCHOOL   THEN AND NOW

People may have a strong memory of relief or regret about leaving school.

While some people may have had no more than the minimum schooling, others may have been able to continue in secondary education past the school leaving age and beyond to further study or have gone back to education later on.

They may like to compare the opportunities they had with those available to school children now.

WHAT I LIKED BEST AT SCHOOL   ASKING AROUND THE GROUP/ FINISHING ACTIVITY

Ask everyone to say what they liked best about their school days and make a connection with what they like now. An example would be *'I used to like history at school, and now I like history plays on television'*. Or *'I did not like school much, but I liked my school friends and I still have good friends'*.

THE MOST USEFUL THING I LEARNED AT SCHOOL   FINISHING ACTIVITY

Ask everyone in turn to say one useful thing they learned at school.

5. THE NEIGHBOURHOOD

Some people have very strong memories of the neighbourhood they lived in as a child, particularly if they mainly stayed in one area, and they may remain very attached to it.

This subject brings out the differences in people's backgrounds and can be used to celebrate the variety. Be aware of the possibility that some people may not want to reveal that their upbringing was very different from others in the group. Take care also not to leave out anyone who moved frequently and who may not be able to remember any one area clearly.

MY NEIGHBOURHOOD

PROMPTED REMINISCENCE/ STARTING ACTIVITY

As a starting point, ask people to describe the sort of neighbourhood they lived in as children.

USEFUL PROMPTS:

- What country were they brought up in?
- Did they live in a town, suburb, village or in the countryside?
- What sort of accommodation did they live in: a house, cottage or flat?
- What were the surroundings like?

GOING BACK IN IMAGINATION

ASKING ROUND THE GROUP

Suggest that people imagine themselves standing outside the front door of the place they lived as a child and ask each in turn to describe briefly what they can remember about what they would see: the view, any buildings nearby, people doing things, streets or fields.

THE PEOPLE WHO CAME ALONG THE STREET

PROMPTED REMINISCENCE

In the towns, at a time when few people had cars, a great many sales and delivery people came round the houses.

Ask people to remember who came down their road. Make a list with descriptions. Some suggestions are: milkman, bread delivery boy, butcher's boy, coal man, ice cream seller, muffin man, laundry man, chimney sweep, knife grinder, cats meat man, street musician, rag and bone man.

Many of these would have a shout, a bell or other way of indicating that they were about. Find out from members of the group what these were.

People brought up in the country or outside Britain may have memories of other people who provided house to house services. Encourage these memories too.

You can extend the topic also to other people associated with the neighbourhood such as 'local characters', for instance, gossips, people with on-going quarrels, nosy neighbours.

NEIGHBOURHOOD CHILDREN

PROMPTED REMINISCENCE

Talk about the games which were played outside by neighbourhood children, such as hop scotch, skipping, bowling hoops. See also the section on CHILDREN AT PLAY.
People often like to remember the naughty things children did around their area. With very little prompting people will laugh over the occasions they knocked on someone's front door and ran away, and other such misdeeds. They may remember special, perhaps secret, places they played in or places which were frightening or forbidden to them as children.

THE CORNER SHOP

PROMPTED REMINISCENCE

The local shop in towns and the village shop in rural areas was sometimes an important community focus. Ask people if there was a local shop which they remember well from childhood. The shop may have been the first place they were allowed to go to alone as a small child. Prompt memories about what their local shop looked like outside and in, how it was arranged, who served there, what was sold, how customers were greeted and whether it was a place where news was exchanged.

THE GROCER

READ A QUOTATION

This memory is about serving in a grocer's shop; see what memories it prompts:

'In them days a shop didn't come in like it does today. You had to weigh your own sugar up, make your own sugar bags, they were always blue. Things like tapioca and rice were put into brown paper which was a bit thicker. You patted your own butter up, and you weighed everything.'

THE BUTCHER, THE BAKER

PROMPTED REMINISCENCE

Buying food at butchers, bakers, greengrocers, grocers shops was different in the past. Ask people what they remember about what going into a shop used to be like.

Prompt them with questions about how the shopkeepers served their customers, how the shops were arranged, what the shop windows looked like, how purchases were weighed and packaged, who took the money.

Local markets and pubs are sometimes also a good source of vivid memories.

MAKE A PICTURE

DRAWING

You can make an impromptu (or more considered) picture of a neighbourhood scene by getting people to make a drawing.

Encourage them to make a picture of what they can remember of their neighbourhood and include pictures of the people who came round the houses selling things and children playing outside.

You could then group the pictures to make a composite neighbourhood scene.

If people cannot draw, do so yourself, asking for descriptions of the buildings, people, and natural objects which are remembered and putting in as much detail as possible.

WHERE WE USED TO LIVE

MAPS/DISPLAY MAKING

Have a map of your local area, a road map of the British Isles, and an atlas of the world so that people can locate the place(s) they lived in as children. Get some more detailed maps of countries other than Britain if you need them.

Make a display of photocopies of the relevant parts of the maps, with labels indicating where different group members lived and perhaps a written memory alongside. If people moved about, show this too with several labels. You can also mark special journeys people made to find work, to go on holiday or to be evacuated. Add photographs or postcards to make an interesting and decorative exhibition.

You can also include labels to show where people live now and where it is that they are meeting together.

A VISIT BACK HOME

OUTING

Street names and pubs often remain unchanged even when other aspects of an area are substantially altered. An outing to a familiar neighbourhood will stimulate many memories.

WHAT THIS AREA USED TO BE LIKE

USING PICTURES/ THEN AND NOW

If several members of the group came from the same small area, see if they can remember what the area used to be like and how it has changed. You may be able to borrow books showing old pictures of the local area. Ask at the library. In some places reprints of old picture postcards are available.

Prompt people to remember what shops there used to be, whether there was somewhere to have a cup of tea, whether there were cinemas or dance halls, even who lived where. Some land-marks, such as pubs and churches, may have not changed at all.

NEIGHBOURLINESS

THEN AND NOW

People often complain that nowadays neighbours are less friendly than they used to be. You can encourage a discussion about the reality of such a remark through memories of close relationships and helpful neighbours or feuds between neighbours and unfriendliness.

With the group members, list on a large sheet of paper the features of good neighbours and bad neighbours. There is likely to be some disagreement, for instance some people will see that being able to borrow money from neighbours is a good thing, others will see it as a bad one.

This discussion might lead on to a discussion about how the group members can be good neighbours or friends to each other in the present.

MAKE UP A STORY

STORY TELLING

Make a list of the characters a street or village is never without. Base it on some of the sort of people remembered in previous discussions.

Some ideas are: the gossip who know everyone's business, the bad tempered person, the person with the immaculate garden, the person who is always helpful to others, the person who is especially kind to children, the person children are afraid of.

Then take turns to make up and perhaps write down a story about events in the street on, say, a sunny Sunday afternoon.

STREET PARTY

PROMPTED REMINISCENCE

Some people remember the excitement of open air street parties held in towns to celebrate the end of the war. See if you can find an equivalent communal celebration for people who lived elsewhere.

Prompt people to remember what preparations had to be made: what furniture was brought out into the street, what food was provided and who made it, whether there were special entertainments for children, whether there was singing and what was sung.

WHAT I LIKE ABOUT WHERE I LIVE NOW

FINISHING ACTIVITY

Ask people to say one thing they like about where they live now.

THE LOCAL SONG

MUSIC/FINISHING ACTIVITY

Some places have songs associated with them. Try to identify an appropriate song for the people in the group to sing at the end of the session. See if you can find a local song for each member of the group. The group members will probably be able to make suggestions.

Some examples of songs with a local connection: *'Maybe it's because I'm a Londoner', 'On Ilkley Moor baht 'at', 'In Dublin's fair city', 'Jamaica farewell'.*

6. HIGH DAYS AND HOLIDAYS

This topic provides an opportunity to talk about the special days which people remember from their childhood: religious festivals, celebrations at home or at school, and national and local holidays.

As well as the festivals celebrated once a year, you can also discuss what happened on the weekly day of rest.

Use this theme to draw out the differences in people's lives as well as the similarities. It is important to regard people as experts in their own culture and in the way they regard it.

MY FAVOURITE DAY OF THE YEAR

ASKING AROUND THE GROUP/ STARTING ACTIVITY

To start with, ask everyone round the group to say whether when they were a child there were favourite days of the year which were special. Prompt them by asking about days of religious festivals such as Christmas, New Year, Jewish New Year, Chinese New Year, Carnival, Mardi Gras, Diwali. Also secular days such as May Day, Pancake Day, Guy Fawkes, Empire Day, Independence Day, and celebrations associated with bringing in the harvest.

WHAT MY SPECIAL DAY WAS LIKE

PROMPTED REMINISCENCE

You can prompt memories about any of the festivals by using the following as a starting point for questions. Focus on one festival if it was part of the experience of everyone in the group. If people's experiences are more varied, include memories of various times.

- ■ What preparations were made in advance?
- ■ Was the home prepared - cleaned or decorated?
- ■ Were special clothes made to wear?
- ■ Was special food made?
- ■ How far in advance were preparations started?
- ■ What happened first when you woke up in the morning of the special day?

■ Describe the activities of the day.

■ Can you remember any thing unusual which happened one year?

MAKE A PICTURE   DRAWING

Supply people with paper and drawing equipment and ask them to draw their memories of a special festival which they celebrated as a child. If they cannot draw themselves, do a drawing for them as they describe what to include.

Another idea is get people to design a card based on memories to send to mark the occasion.

Try to discourage them from drawing or describing a stereotyped picture, such as those commercially produced, but one based on their own memories.

MUSICAL ASSOCIATIONS   MUSIC AND SOUNDS

Using the list of festivals and celebrations, ask the group to remember whether there is particular music that they associate with the day. National holidays as well as religious holidays often involve singing songs. Prompt people to remember where the songs were sung, by whom, whether the singers were accompanied. Encourage the group members to sing as much of the songs as they can remember.

Try to find tapes of the music to play on subsequent occasions.

HOLDING A CELEBRATION   PRACTICAL ACTIVITY

Members of the reminiscence group may like to take a lead in celebrating festivals other than those normally marked by the group. The dates of many religious festivals vary from year to year, so check those for the current year. If within your group there are several people of different cultures, make an annual programme of festivals to celebrate.

When preparing for a particular celebration ask the members of the group who know about it to make suggestions about food to prepare, decorations to make, and appropriate ways of marking the occasion.

Use the preparations and the celebration to explain to other people the significance of the celebration.

MAKE CULTURAL LINKS   OUTING

If someone is isolated from their cultural roots and would like to celebrate a particular festival, see if you can arrange for them to join in with an appropriate group elsewhere or for an outside group to visit them.

MAKE A DISPLAY   USING OBJECTS/DISPLAY MAKING

Many religious festivals are linked with the seasons. You could decide to make an occasional or regular seasonal display which includes religious, national and natural objects.

For instance a winter display could include some snowdrops, some bare twigs, a symbol of Christmas such as a crib, a symbol of Hanukkah such as a candlebra, symbols, such as lights or sweets, associated with the Sikh celebration of the birth of Gobind Singh, a lump of coal and a mound of salt representing New Year in the north of England and Scotland, plus other things appropriate to your group.

Ask the group members for ideas. They may be able to lend items for the display too.

THE SPECIAL DAY OF THE WEEK   PROMPTED REMINISCENCE

Many of the activities described in this section can also be used to prompt memories of Friday, Saturday or Sunday rituals, routines and prohibitions.

SUNDAY TEA   TASTE, TOUCH AND SMELL

In a predominantly British group arrange a Sunday tea sitting around a table. Provide to eat the sort of things that the reminiscence group remember having eaten on Sundays,. for instance :

■ ham ■ tongue ■ crumpets ■ muffins,
■ sardines ■ jelly and custard ■ home-made cake.

BIRTH, DEATH AND MARRIAGE   PROMPTED REMINISCENCE

Another aspect of cultural practice is associated with rituals surrounding birth, coming of age, marriage and death. Encourage people to talk about their memories of these from their childhood.

The **COURTING AND MARRIAGE SECTION** suggests several ideas for activities around marriage.

TIMES CHANGE   THEN AND NOW

The ways of marking high days and holy days do not necessarily remain static over the decades. Some people will be able to talk about the way practices altered from their childhood, to their young adult life, to their older adult life and now. See what people think about this and ask also how their children and grandchildren, if they have them, follow the traditions.

7. A DAY OUT

In the past, summer holidays as we know them were very unusual, but many people will remember going on day trips to the seaside, or to the country, to a temple, picnic place or beauty spot, or just for a bicycle ride. They may have gone with their family, with school or a club, or, as they got older, with friends.

This topic would be a good preparation for taking people on a real day out.

The activities described here focus particularly on going to visit the seaside and going on a picnic. As this topic is also an opportunity to talk about ways of travelling, ideas involving travel are also included.

There are many memories and photographs on this topic in the Age Exchange book, "The Time Of Our Lives".

WHERE PEOPLE USED TO GO

LISTING ACTIVITY/STARTING ACTIVITY

Introduce the topic by asking people to say where they used to like to go to for a day out when they were young. Make a list on a large sheet of paper. Ask people to name particular places as well as types of places.

A TRIP I REMEMBER

LISTING ACTIVITY/STARTING ACTIVITY

Ask everyone to think of their favourite sort of trip and prompt memories by asking:

- Choose a place you went to on a day out
- Where did you go?
- How did you get there?
- Whom did you go with?
- What did you do when you got there?
- What was there to eat?
- What clothes did you wear?
- How did you get home?

If members of the group are fairly expert reminiscers, you could ask everyone to shut their eyes, while you slowly ask the questions, and think about the answers to themselves. Then give everyone a chance to describe what they thought of.

If people are unlikely to be able to do the exercise like that, then use these questions as prompts one at a time and allow plenty of time for replies.

MAKE A DISPLAY   MAPS

If the group members all grew up in a similar area, ask them where the favourite local places to go for a day out were, and mark them on a map.

Make a display using the map and written memories of outings as described to you or written by group members. If you can, add personal photographs of people in the group and relevant picture postcards.

A DAY AT THE SEASIDE   USING PICTURES

Make a collection of seaside postcards and some pictures from holiday brochures to use as a starting point for discussion about people's memories of being at the seaside. Ask people to bring to the session their own photographs if they have them.

Hand the pictures round and talk about the memories they prompt.

A DAY AT THE SEASIDE   STORY TELLING

Start people off making a story about a day out at the sea with ...
"It was bright and sunny morning when the day of the outing finally arrived. Joan Smith and her neighbour Rose Brown and their five children were up early to get ready to go to the sea for the day ..."
Prompt people to suggest
■   what they took with them
■   what they wore
■   how they got there
■ what they did when they were at the seaside.
Intertwine everyone's suggestions of whatever sort of seaside place they are thinking of. If the story telling goes well, write it down or encourage people to write their own stories, based on their memories.

THE SOUNDS OF THE SEASIDE   MUSIC & SOUND/STORIES

Ask the group members to remember and make as many sounds associated with the seaside as they can. Some ideas are:
the wind, the waves, seagulls, fair ground music, Punch and Judy, the band on the pier, ice cream sellers and other sales people, steamer hooter, steam train, children playing.
Make up a story to tell interspersed with everyone making the appropriate sounds.

SEASIDE FOOD
TOUCH, TASTE & SMELL/ PRACTICAL ACTIVITY

Bring to the group some food associated with trips to the seaside to smell and eat. Suggestions are: jellied eels, cockles, whelks, mussels, coconut ice, ice cream cornets, a packet of chips. Talk about other snack foods and see if you can bring them to the session or make them together.

If you are unable to make or buy the sort of snacks which people remember, ask them for detailed descriptions.

SAND AND SHELLS
TOUCH AND SMELL

For people who are not verbally responsive, you could involve them in an activity which entails them feeling sand and shells.

Prepare a large strong tray or box with some fine sand and have available some sea shells and pebbles. Encourage people to join you as you make patterns in the sand with your fingers and decorate the sand with shells, pebbles and anything else you have collected. Talk to them as you do it about the feel of the sand and the shape of the shells.

Collect some seaweed and some sand castle flags next time you go to the coast to have available for your sand tray.

The seashells may smell salty and if you have collected some seaweed it may smell too. Encourage people to smell them and talk about the sea.

DECORATING BOXES
PRACTICAL ACTIVITY

Someone may remember decorating small boxes with shells. If people would like to try this for themselves, collect or buy a variety of shells and find some suitable small boxes. Use strong glue.

LISTENING TO THE SEA
HANDLING AN OBJECT

If you have a conch shell or another sort of spiral shaped shell, ask people to put it to their ear and imagine that they can hear the waves. Ask them what the sound of the waves makes them think of.

PICNIC
PROMPTED REMINISCENCE

Collect some suitable props, for instance a rug or a check table cloth, a basket or hamper, a thermos flask, a sun hat, a cotton handkerchief knotted at the corners. Arrange the objects on the floor and sit yourself on the floor amongst them.

Ask people what it reminds them of. Then ask them to describe what an ideal picnic spot should have (a tree to climb, a view, a stream to paddle in, a place which sells food, somewhere to fly a kite) and what they remember doing on a picnic they went on.

Someone may have a memory of a particularly enjoyable or disastrous picnic.

A PICNIC GROUP

DRAMA ACTIVITY

This follows on well from the previous activity. Leave the rug and objects in the middle of the floor and stay there yourself. Ask people to suggest who else might be on the picnic with you (family members or friends for instance). Ask members of the group to play parts and set up some dialogue.

Ideas of possible scenes: a family group with a child who has got sand on the food, a group of friends who cannot agree whether to go on or turn back, a family group at the seaside discussing what to play on the beach, a bull appearing in a corner of the field.

Help each other to think of appropriate dialogue.

IN THE PICNIC BASKET

ASKING ROUND THE GROUP

Ask the group members in turn what they would have wanted there to be in the basket for them.

Go round the group several times asking what sort of food, sandwiches, what drink, fruit, confectionary or sweets they would take.

Start off with your own favourite type of sandwich or picnic food.

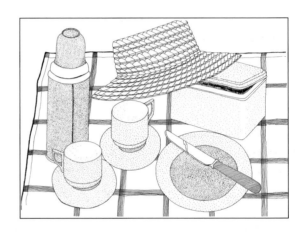

PLAYING GAMES

LISTING

Playing such games as cricket, badminton, football is associated with going on a picnic or being by the sea. Ask people to remember all the games they used to play and make a list. Ask for details about the games and the equipment people used.

You could extend this to games played to pass the time on the journey, such as *"I Spy"*, *"Pub Cricket"* and *"My Grandmother Went to Market"*. Ask people to describe the rules of one of the games.

PLAN A DAY OUT

AN OUTING

Plan a real outing in discussion with the reminiscence group. Decide where to go - a local park, beauty spot, seaside, or perhaps just the garden. Decide what food to take and if possible make it together with the group. Then go off and enjoy the outing.

On the outing look around at people playing outdoor games and identify and talk about what they are playing.

French cricket with a soft ball may be a possible game for a not very mobile group of people to play.

FLYING A KITE

AN OUTING

In many parts of the world, kite making and flying is a popular childhood activity and some of the group may have made and flown their own kites. The group could try to do this, following instructions from one member or from a book. Even from a seated position, it is quite exhilarating to feel a kite in the air pulling at the string.

HAVE A PICNIC

TOUCH, TASTE AND SMELL

Pack up some food and take a few people out to the nearest fresh air to eat it. Provide something interesting or unusual to drink, for instance cider, dandelion and burdock, sasparilla, vimto, fizzy lemonade.

Encourage people to feel the sunshine or the breeze. Suggest they take deep breaths of fresh air.

Draw people's attention to things around them such as flowers, grass, trees, sunshine, birds. Talk about the weather and the season.

MAKING A NATURE TABLE

USING OBJECTS

For people who rarely go outside, make a seasonal display along the lines of a primary school nature table and show and describe the objects to people. Encourage them to smell and handle things and to contribute or suggest appropriate items.

A spring table might include some pussy willows, catkins or sticky buds, a bunch of daffodils or primroses, a birds' nest, a bird's egg, perhaps some Easter chicks.

A summer table might include a bunch of roses, some honeysuckle, a bag of cherries, sea shells, a feather.

For an autumn table look for some autumn berries, hips, and brown leaves, some apples, some hops, michaelmas daisies, blackberries, chestnuts.

A winter table is more difficult but some bare branches, some holly with berries, a bunch or pot of snowdrops, a pile of nuts, bird food, a mousetrap might start you off.

THE JOURNEY

PROMPTED REMINISCENCE

A chance to remember in more detail ways of travelling to a day out can follow on from some of the earlier discussions.

Start by asking people what means of transport they remember using to go on a day out.

PROMPTS:
- bicycle
- train
- car
- cart
- charabanc
- bus
- boat
- lorry
- pony and trap

Then go on to ask for more detailed descriptions.

TRAVELLING BY TRAIN

Your local library will probably have a book with pictures of steam trains.

Ask people to describe their memories of travelling by train.

See if anyone can remember what the inside of a railway carriage used to be like.

Prompt them to describe the upholstery, the luggage rack made of string, the small rack for umbrellas, the pictures on the compartment walls, the notices on the windows and door, the smell and sound of a steam train.

Go on to descriptions of the view from the window.

A CROWDED COMPARTMENT

DRAMA ACTIVITY

If the group are prepared to try a little spontaneous drama arrange some people in a row opposite each other as if they were in a railway carriage, include yourself in this group.

Say you are a group of people going out for the day in a bumpy train. Bob up and down in your chairs a little.

Start the action going by, for instance, having a discussion about having the window open or shut, or about someone taking up too much room on the seat, or about someone eating raw onion in their sandwich and how it is making the carriage smell, about going through a tunnel and smuts coming into the compartment.

Get everyone to make suggestions and join in, even if from the side lines.

A drama activity like this could be used for other modes of transport such as travelling in a charabanc or cart.

A REAL STEAM TRAIN JOURNEY

AN OUTING

If there are train enthusiasts in the group and there is within reach a steam train preservation group which runs real trains, arrange to take some people on a visit to see and even make a journey on a steam train. Train carriages may be hard to climb into for the less agile, so check accessibility first.

RIDING A BICYCLE   PROMPTED MEMORIES

The pre-war period was a great period for bicycle riding both for work and for leisure.

Ask people if they used to ride a bicycle and prompt the discussion with such comments as:

- What sort of bicycle did they have?
- How did they acquire it?
- Did they have to save up and buy it?
- Can they remember how much it cost?
- Can they describe how many gears it had and any other special features?
- Did they look after it very carefully?
- What did they wear to ride their bicycle?
- Did they have a bicycle lamp and if so, what sort?

A DAY OUT BY BIKE   STORY TELLING

If there are former keen cyclists in the group ask them to describe an expedition they went on.

A GOING HOME SONG   MUSIC /FINISHING ACTIVITIES

Ask people for suggestions of a song suitable to sing on the way back tired from an outing. Sing it together to end the session. Some suggestions are: 'I'll give you one oh! Green grow the rushes oh!', 'Polly wally doodle', 'Michael row the boat ashore' and 'One man went to mow'.

SUMMING UP   GOING ROUND THE GROUP

Describe briefly the memories which have been discussed during the session making sure you mention something for everyone.

8. DRESSING UP AND LOOKING GOOD

Remembering what one used to look like is a strong link with one's younger self.

Focus this discussion on young adulthood, the age range from sixteen to the early twenties.

Some men and women have surprisingly strong memories of clothes they wore for particular special occasions.

SETTING THE SCENE

HANDLING OBJECTS/STARTING ACTIVITY

Use an attractive hand bag, preferably an evening bag, and put in it some of the sort of items which a teenage girl would take on an evening out, such as a lace handkerchief, a powder compact, a lipstick, some hair pins.

Tell, or remind, the group that the topic of the session is dressing up and ask them what they would expect to find in a hand bag like the one you have.

Show them what is in it, and ask them what they themselves would have taken on an evening out.

Ask men what they would have had in their pockets.

CHANGING FASHIONS   USING PICTURES

Discuss what sort of clothes people used to wear in the years after they had left school. Have as triggers some pictures of twenties, thirties, forties fashions to show people. It is important to get the right period for the members of the group, so work out in which era they were in their late teens or early twenties and get appropriate books from the library.

People may have photographs of themselves to bring to the session.

MY FIRST GROWN UP OUTFIT   ASKING ROUND THE GROUP

Ask everyone in turn to describe their first grown up outfit, or another special outfit. Ask for as much detail as possible about colour, material, cut, and accessories, how their hair was done, what shoes they wore, what underwear, and whether they wore make-up.

MY SMARTEST CLOTHES

DRAWING

Following the previous exercise, you could get people to draw the special clothes they remembered. Or draw for them following their descriptions, asking for lots of information so you can draw as accurately as possible.

HAVE YOU GOT A CLEAN HANDKERCHIEF?

THINGS LEARNED BY HEART

Ask the members of the group whether their mothers had characteristic instructions about being properly dressed for going out.

Typical examples of mothers' instructions are:

- **Wear clean underwear in case you are knocked down by a bus**
- **Remember to take a clean handkerchief**
- **Take two handkerchiefs - 'one for blow and one for show'**
- **Have you polished your shoes?**
- **Are your cuffs clean?**

People may also remember parental prohibitions for instance about make-up:
"take that muck off your face".'

MATERIALS & TEXTURES

TOUCH AND SMELL

Make a collection of interesting things to feel which are connected with the topic. Suggestions are: soft kid gloves, silk stockings, stiff starched detached collars, a piece of lace, a silk scarf, a chiffon scarf and various types of material, for instance, velvet, satin, brocade, crepe, chiffon, fur.

Encourage people who cannot say much to touch and stroke the items, while you talk about the qualities of softness or smoothness and describe the colours. People who can talk can be asked whether they wore things like the items.

THINGS WHICH HAVE A SMELL

SMELL

Moth balls and Eau de Cologne are easily available items which have a strong smell and are associated with this theme. Encourage people to take a sniff and ask them what the smell reminds them of.

TRADE NAMES

PROMPTED REMINISCENCE

The trade names of perfume and make-up are very evocative of the past. Ask the group if they can remember old trade names or lipstick colours. Here are the names of some old fashioned scents to start you off: Californian Poppy, Fulnana, Ashes of Roses, Evening in Paris, 4711 (called four seven eleven).

You could suggest that people shut their eyes and try to remember the smell of their favourite scent.

USING CURLING-TONGS

HANDLING OBJECTS

Have a pair of old hair tongs and ask people to explain to you how they were heated and show you on someone's hair how they were used. Similar sorts of tongs were used in many parts of the world either to curl or to straighten hair.

CHANGING HAIR STYLES

DRAWING

Women's and men's hair styles have changed greatly over the century. It would be interesting to ask everyone what sort of hair style they had at different ages.

You could record, perhaps with a drawing or a picture, who had long hair when they were young, what colour it was, who had a bob or a marcel wave, who parted their hair in the middle, who wore brilliantine, who remembers their first perm, what sort of hair style they have now.

Include changes in the men's beards and moustaches as well as their hair. Ask if anyone can remember handlebar, waxed or tooth-brush moustaches, goatee beards, sideburns and number one, number two, number three haircuts.

MAKE UP

PROMPTED REMINISCENCE

Using make-up is a very personal habit and you may find that attitudes to its use vary widely in a group. People may well like to discuss what attitudes were when they were young and whether views have changed during their life time.

If you have modern make-up available, some people may like to try it on themselves, especially if they do not normally have the opportunity. Care is needed here, as others will probably hate the idea.

SHAVING
PROMPTED REMINISCENCE

Men may remember the routines related to shaving when they were younger and what sort of soap and razor they used and how possible it was to get hot water.

Some men may be able to describe going to the barber for a shave and recall particular incidents.

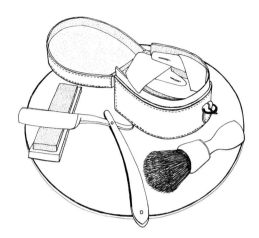

HATS
PROMPTED REMINISCENCE/PRACTICAL ACTIVITY

Discuss with the group whether they used to wear hats, scarves or head wear more than they do now. If it seems that they did, ask everyone, both men and women, to describe the favourite sort of head wear which they used to have.

If you have anyone in the group who worked as a milliner or made or dressed their own hats, they may be able to tell you in detail how it was done. Make a collection of old hats and millinery materials (such as ribbons, feathers, cloth flowers, veiling), and the people who know about millinery can show the others the sort of things they used to do. Ask them what sort of materials you should collect.

PREPARING TO GO OUT FOR A SPECIAL OCCASION
PROMPTED REMINISCENCE

Ask people to describe getting ready for a very special outing when they were young adults. They may have washed their hair, gone to the barber for a haircut and shave, pressed their clothes, brushed their coat, checked for any loose threads, put on make up or hair cream.

FASHION HORRORS
STORY TELLING

People may enjoy remembering times when they wore really uncomfortable or totally unsutable clothes or shoes in order to look smart.. Or they may have disaster stories about times when they thought were looking good but the clothing shrank in rain or crucial elastic snapped.

AN IMAGINARY FASHION PARADE
DRAMA ACTIVITY

Suggest that everyone imagines that they are appearing in a fashion parade as their younger selves. They can choose to imagine themselves wearing an outfit they really had, an outrageous fantasy one, or something they remember longing for.

Ask them to describe what they are wearing in the style of a fashion parade commentary. For instance *'Florrie is wearing....'*.
People might want to actually parade around, or remain sitting still.

SPECIAL CLOTHES FOR PARTICULAR ACTIVITIES

PROMPTED REMINISCENCE

Some people may remember clothing which was appropriate for particular occasions. For instance, ask people what sort of clothes they would have worn for: church, dancing, a job interview, office or factory work, work in service, housework, a summer expedition, or different sporting activities.

FABRICS

MAKING A LIST

Start by looking at the group and naming the sorts of materials which their clothes are made of. Then go on and see how many different sorts of fabrics people remember wearing or knowing about in the past. The names alone are very evocative, but ask people what sort of clothing was made out of each and whether they can remember any particular items. Former dress makers or drapery or clothing shop assistants will enjoy this.

One reminiscence group was able to name over seventy different fabrics which they had been familiar with. Here are a few names to start with: chiffon, crepe de Chine, georgette, muslin, ninon, organdie, velveteen.

BUYING OR MAKING CLOTHES

PROMPTED REMINISCENCE

You can ask also about memories of dress-making, saving up to buy clothes, having things made for one, borrowing or being given second hand things, cast-offs or hand-me-downs and going shopping for clothes.

DRESSING UP AND LOOKING GOOD

PRACTICAL ACTIVITY

Suggest that the group members dress in their best clothes, polish their shoes, do their hair carefully, put on some jewellery to attend the session.

Discuss the differences and similarities between what they do now to get ready and what they used to do when they were younger.

COMPARISONS WITH THE PRESENT

THEN AND NOW

Describe with the group the sort of clothes young people wear now to go out.

Draw on what you and the group have observed in the streets, in their family, or in the media.

Discuss similarities and differences with what they wore when they were young.

THEN AND NOW

FINISHING ACTIVITY

Sum up at the end of a session with a few of the memories which each person had and add in something about what they are wearing now. For instance: *'Rose remembered the green suit she bought when she first went out to work. And now she is wearing a green checked dress.'*

9. AN EVENING OUT

The way people spent an evening out as a young person will depend very much on where they were living, what facilities were available, what freedoms they were allowed and how much time and money they had.

Discover how members of the group did spend their leisure time and use the ideas provided here or adapt them to something more appropriate. The detailed ideas relate to dancing and going to the cinema, two extremely popular leisure time activities for young people.

WHAT DID WE DO?   MAKING A LIST/STARTING ACTIVITY

Ask the group members to look back to when they were young, between the ages of fifteen and twenty-five say, and remember the sort of activities they did when they were not working, when they had a night out with friends.

PROMPTS: ■ dancing ■ cinema ■ theatre ■ listening to music ■ taking part in music or amateur dramatics ■ evening classes ■ going to the pub ■ visiting friends.

Then with the group decide which to focus on first and discuss in more detail.

HOW MUCH TIME DID WE HAVE?

PROMPTED REMINISCENCE

In order to acknowledge the different experiences, in particular those of people who had responsibilities quite young or little leisure time for other reasons, ask people to say how often they were able to go out and whether they were able to do whatever they liked.

DANCING

READ A QUOTATION

❝ We used to go dancing at the Town Hall, the Labour Club, and any clubs around that had dancing. The fellows used to stand all up by the door and the girls would be sitting around. Then, when the music started, they'd just go up to whoever they fancied. We used to dance every dance - quick step, foxtrot, one step - oh we used to enjoy it!❞

Read this memory and see if the memories of the people in the group are similar or different.

DANCES I REMEMBER

MAKING A LIST

Make a list of all the dances which people know with a few comments about each.

PROMPTS (if necessary)
- waltz ■ quick step ■ foxtrot ■ tango ■ charleston
- black bottom ■ jitterbug ■ rock and roll ■ palais glide
- Lambeth Walk ■ twostep ■ velita ■ polka ■ hokey-cokey
- various country dances ■ national dances.

GOING DANCING

PROMPTED REMINISCENCE

Discuss where people used to dance, what sort of occasions they were, whether formal or informal, private or public.

Ask them how they got there, how much it cost, and whether they went in their smart dancing clothes and shoes.

Ask people how they learned to dance, whether they picked up dances from a young age, whether they were taught by a friend or member of their family, or whether they went to dancing lessons.

You can also ask about how they practised dance steps, with whom, and whether they had a gramophone to practise with.

WILL YOU DANCE WITH ME?

DRAMA IDEA

A discussion about how a boy asked a girl to dance can easily be turned into a few minutes acting.

Prompt someone to play the part of a shy, or else very confident, boy going up to two girls. The girls can be gossiping about which one of them he is going to ask to dance.

The person playing the boy has to decide how to phrase the invitation to dance with him and the girl asked has to make a negative or positive response.

Check out with other members of the group whether what the 'actors' said and how they reacted accords with their memory of what might have been said.

WHAT TO WEAR — PROMPTED REMINISCENCE/DRAWING

Women who were keen dancers, often had a surprising number of dance dresses. See if they can remember and describe in detail one of their dresses including what it looked like, what they wore with it, and whether they made or bought it.

Ask the men too what they wore. Ask them to remember an evening suit or best suit and see if they wore gloves to dance in, and a white silk scarf round their neck.

Include also the memories of people who wore national costume for dancing.

Drawing often assists the memory. If you draw the clothing as it is described, you will have to ask for details about neckline, waist position, shape, sleeve and hem length, exact colour shade.

The library may be able to supply you with books with pictures of clothes which will prompt memories.

MY IDEAL PARTNER — ASKING ROUND THE GROUP

Ask everyone in turn to say who their dream dancing partner would be. There is a chance here to imagine going out dancing with Fred Astaire, Rudolph Valentino, or Ginger Rogers, or some private dancing idol of their own.

IMPROMPTU DANCING — PRACTICAL ACTIVITY

End the session with a little dancing of the sort discussed during the session. If you do not know how to dance allow yourself to be taught by group members.

If standing up and moving is not possible, you can encourage people to dance with their hands.

DANCING WITH PUPPETS — DRAMA ACTIVITY

A simple non verbal way of conveying the idea of dancing is to have two puppets or dolls and make them dance together as you hum or play a tune. Encourage someone to take the puppets from you and continue the mood.

DANCE MUSIC — MUSIC

Play a tape of some dance music appropriate to the period of the youth of the people in the group, for instance Charleston dance music for people young in the 20s, and dance band music of the 30s and 40s.

The popular music people know tends to be related closely to their age. The dance music popular in the 1940s will prompt memories of people who were young then, and may have no associations for people who are older or younger.

A reminiscence group is quite likely to include quite an age range, so you need to have a variety of music available.

If you are keen on music and you think the reminiscence group members would enjoy it, make a tape of different types of dance music. The tape can either be of dance tunes or types of dances (a waltz, a foxtrot, a charleston). See if people can identify the music on the tape.

GOING DANCING   OUTING

You might like to follow a reminiscence session on dancing with some real dancing, either by arranging a dance yourselves, or by going out to somewhere locally which holds dances. Another idea is to invite a couple of dancers from a local dance school or evening class to visit the group.

MY FAVOURITE FILM

ASKING ROUND THE GROUP

See if everyone can name a film they really enjoyed in their youth.

This might lead to a discussion about the different types of films people preferred:

- romances
- adventure films
- serial films

(films which continued with the same characters and adventures, week after week)

- musicals
- comedies
- history films
- news films
- cartoons.

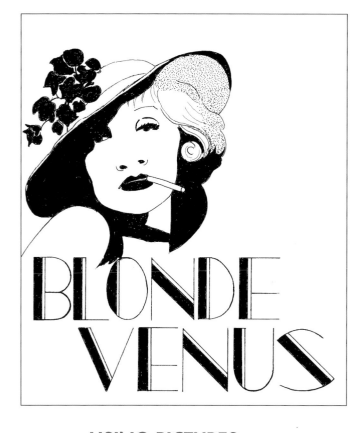

FAVOURITE STARS   USING PICTURES

Pin ups and crushes are not a modern phenomenon. Ask people who their favourite stars were and whether they were really keen on them.

Show them some pictures of stars and see if people can remember the films they appeared in. It is possible to buy sets of film star pictures and also postcards of stars and buy or borrow books about old films.

With group members or individuals, you could also make a film star scrap book, using pictures of old stars from magazines with some contemporary stars also. Making a scrap book is a reminiscence activity in itself as many people made scrapbooks in their youth.

GOING TO THE CINEMA

PROMPTED REMINISCENCE

Ask people to describe what going to see a film was like.

PROMPTS:

- Describe the building inside and outside.
- What the attendants and usherettes were like.
- Whether they had to queue for tickets.
- How much it cost to get in and whether they could afford the price easily or not.
- What programmes consisted of: a first feature film, a second feature film, advertisements, news items, cartoons.
- Whether there was live music on a cinema organ.
- Where they liked to sit.
- Whether they bought anything to eat.
- Who they went with.
- Whether they ever worked in a cinema or knew someone who did.

CINEMAS

PROMPTED REMINISCENCE/MAPS

If the members of your group spent their youth in approximately the same local area, see if they can remember where all the cinemas were. If you are much younger than they are, you will probably be surprised by how many cinemas there used to be.

PROMPTS : traditional cinema names may stir some memories :

- Odeon
- Gaumont
- Splendid
- Rex
- Electric Palace
- 'the fleapit '
- Regent
- Roxy
- Plaza
- Granada.

You could then get a map of the local area and mark the sites of the cinemas remembered, perhaps adding a written memory, to make a display.

THE NEWSREEL

PROMPTED REMINISCENCE

Before television was widespread, a cinema programme often included a news programme, called a news reel. During the war and at other times of dramatic news it was an important source of information.

See if people can remember and describe seeing news about any particular historic events at the cinema. Pathe News films have been reissued on video and are readily available.

WATCHING A FILM

PRACTICAL ACTIVITY

The discussion of favourite films could lead to suggestions of old films which people want to see again. It might be possible to borrow them on video and arrange a special showing. Include non-English language films if people wish. You could provide the sort of snacks which people remember having in the cinema such as oranges, sweets, pop-corn, peanuts in their shells.

If the members of the group are living in a residential setting where the television set is turned on a lot of the time, you could use the reminiscence discussion to decide with the group if there are any old films being shown on television in the forthcoming week which they would positively like to watch together and perhaps discuss afterwards.

GOING TO A REAL CINEMA   OUTING

See if you can take a group of keen cinema goers to a local cinema or encourage them to go on their own. Aftewrwards discuss the similarities and differences of cinema going today and in the past.

10. GOING OUT TO WORK

Reminiscence groups often consist mainly of women whose prime activity was in the domestic sphere. However many women as well as most men have had paid work at some time of their lives and have learned working skills which they like to talk about.

Working lives may provide material for several sessions. Start perhaps with the first jobs people had and go on to the jobs they regard as most significant for them. An important aspect of the work topic is the moves people made from different parts of Britain and from different places in the world to find employment.

There are suggestions about activities related to war time work in Section 12, LIVING THROUGH THE WAR.

The Age Exchange publication, " My First Job", has interesting memories and pictures on the topic of working life.

ALL THE WORK I HAVE DONE

MAKING A LIST STARTING ACTIVITY

Ask people around the group to describe the work they did when they were younger. Some people may have had many jobs, others may have mainly worked at one trade or profession. Include as work unpaid domestic work - cleaning, cooking, shopping, looking after people.

Point out and encourage people to discuss similarities and differences within the group.

WHAT'S MY LINE?

DRAMA ACTIVITY

Ask people to remember a job they had when they were younger and ask them to mime it to the group so that the others can guess what it was. Start the activity going by doing a simple mime yourself so that people get the idea. Many people will be able to join in with this given help and encouragement. Help people to guess what is being mimed.

MY FIRST JOB

PROMPTED REMINISCENCE

Ask people to describe briefly their first paid work when they had just left school.

Prompt them with questions about such things as:

- How they found the job?
- Whether they had an interview or not?
- How much they got paid?
- What they had to do?
- Where they were living?
- What time they left home for work and when they arrived?
- If they lived at home, whether they had to give money to their mother?
- What the other people were like?
- What they wore?
- What they spent their first pay packet on?

THE TOOLS OF THE TRADE

HANDLING OBJECTS

Make a collection of objects associated with work. Some examples of fairly easily acquired objects are: a scrubbing brush, a yellow duster, a plane for woodwork, hammer and nails, a spade, a typewriter, white or blue workman's overalls, a dark peaked cap, a milk bottle, a butcher's apron, an oil can and an oily cloth, needle and thread.

If you are in an area which had or has a predominant industry such as coal mining, railway work, agricultural work, try to get some objects specifically associated with that industry.

Ask people to talk about the sort of work which they associate with the objects. If anyone was employed in jobs relevant to the objects, encourage them to talk about the various tools of their trade and how they were used. Prompt other people to talk about the tools or equipment they used at work.

TEACHING SOMEONE ELSE

DRAMA IDEA

This activity might follow on from one of the previous ones.

Choose someone who seems to enjoy talking about their work and ask them to remember all the important tasks they had to do.

Say that you are going to pretend to be a young person new to the job and you need to be fully instructed how to do it. Get the group member to show you what to do in as much detail as possible, asking questions to prompt them and moving about as necessary. Make sure that other people in the group are following the action, and look out for opportunities for other people to join in.

Repeat this with other people in the group.

MOVING TO GO TO WORK

PROMPTED REMINISCENCE

Members of the group may have had to leave home as young people to find jobs. They may have come to Britain to work from the Caribbean, Ireland or other parts of the world. Or they may have had to move from the country to the town.

Encourage them to talk about:

■   what they felt about leaving

■   how they were recruited

■   how they travelled, what their first reactions were

■   how they settled down

■   how they found somewhere to live

■   how they made friends

■   how they kept in touch with home.

Be prepared for people to be emotional about moving away from home.

STARTING A NEW JOB

PROMPTED REMINISCENCE

Ask people to remember what it was like starting a new job.
Prompt them with such questions as:

■   How did they feel when they first arrived?

■   Who showed them what to do?

■   How long did it take them to learn what to do?

■   What made them feel more confident?

■   What helped them in the new situation and what did not help them?

You could use such a discussion as a starting point to help people think about new situations they might be facing in the present. You and they might be able to draw some conclusions from what was helpful in new situations in the past to plan for the future.

WORK CLOTHES

DRAWING ACTIVITIES

Provide people with large sheets of paper and drawing equipment and ask them to remember and draw what they wore to work for one of the jobs they had when they were employed.

If people are unable to draw for themselves, do the drawing for them asking them to tell you

what to put in the picture. Ask for detailed descriptions of uniforms or work clothes including shoes, head wear, overalls.

You could prepare for this activity by drawing several large outline figures on sheets of card 'to be dressed' during the session either by drawing, painting or by collage.

A collage activity would be best undertaken once you know what sorts of colours or materials are likely to be needed, so prepare for it with a reminiscence session first in which people talk about the work clothes they remember.

Another idea is to make cut-out clothes with tabs from card to fit on outline figures. As this is like the paper dolls with cut-out clothes which children used to play with, it is a reminiscence activity in itself.

OUR WORKING LIVES

MAKE A DISPLAY

If people are enthusiastic about talking about their working lives, you could decide together to make a small (or more ambitious) display.
The display might include objects associated with work, personal souvenirs such as photographs or certificates, examples of work done, drawings and written accounts.

A TYPICAL DAY AT WORK

PROMPTED REMINISCENCE/ WRITING

A way of prompting detailed memories is to ask people to write or describe what might have happened in a typical working day hour by hour. This approach works well for people who were in service doing domestic work for other people as they often had to start work early and had a very definite routine. See what memories it prompts for people in other work as well.

This activity might be written up like a timetable as a contribution to a display.

THE LOCAL NEWSPAPER

THEN AND NOW

From a current local paper read some of the job advertisements to start a discussion about the sorts of jobs young people do now and what was available when the group members were first looking for work.

THE JOB THAT DOES NOT EXIST ANY MORE

LISTING

Ask the group to remember all the jobs which used to exist and do not any longer, or are much rarer. List the jobs on a large sheet of paper and talk about what people know about them. Some suggestions are:

■ people who came round the streets: lamplighter, muffin man, cats meat man, delivery boy

■ domestic jobs in private households: parlour maid, cook general

■ transport jobs: tram driver, canal man

■ jobs in dress making: millinery, drapery.

GOING FOR AN INTERVIEW

DRAMA IDEA

Try acting out an interview situation between an employer and a young prospective employee. Suggest a job which several people in the group have experience of. The questions asked by the employer and the answers can be suggested by the members of the group.

Plan the situation in advance with the group or try it spontaneously.

At the end, the group can decide whether the young person would have been offered the job and accepted it or not.

HOW THINGS HAVE CHANGED

THEN AND NOW

Prompt a discussion comparing what shop assistants in a large supermarket do today with what the tasks of shop assistants used to be. This would be a particularly appropriate activity if people in the group have worked in shops.

Adapt this idea to other jobs which members of the groups have experience of, for example, domestic work, farm work, office work.

EMPLOYMENT AND UNEMPLOYMENT

PROMPTED REMINISCENCE

The working life of some people in the group may have been marked by periods of employment and unemployment. Ask people about their experience of unemployment and difficulties of finding work. Compare it with your own experience or that of people you know.

THE JOB I LIKED BEST

ASKING ROUND THE GROUP/ FINISHING ACTIVITY

Ask people to say briefly what in their working life (or in their domestic working life) they got the most satisfaction from and why.

11. COURTING AND MARRIAGE

This topic gives people a chance to experience several different feelings: amusement at their past behaviour, love and anger about people whom they used to know, and sadness about people who are dead.

There may be some people in the group who did not marry. You will need to be sensitive to their feelings. They may nevertheless have loved and they may or may not want to talk about it. Remember that some members of your group may not be heterosexual. Their experience in relation to this theme will probably be very different from others in the group and this should be acknowledged positively if they choose to talk about it.

Do not presume that older people no longer have romantic or sexual feelings and do not tease people about their feelings or behaviour in the past or the present.

This section also includes activities about setting up home as an adult.

SING A SONG MUSIC/STARTING OR FINISHING ACTIVITY

There are hundreds of songs on the topic of love.

Two suggestions are *'Love and marriage go together like a horse and carriage'* or *'If you were the only girl in the world and I were the only boy'*.

MEETING SOMEONE SPECIAL   LISTING

For many people growing up, there is a stage before they pair up when young people go to places where they will see members of the opposite sex and be seen by them. In England this is sometimes called 'the monkey parade'.

Make a list with the group of the places local to them when they were young where people went to show themselves off. Some suggestions are: the local park, the band stand, the high street, the dance hall, church, the tennis club, the pub.

Use the listing activity to discuss their memories about these places.

NOT MEETING THE OPPOSITE SEX   PROMPTED REMINISCENCE

In some cultures the freedom to mix is not allowed and eligible members of the opposite sex are only glimpsed, if seen at all. Talk about this too.

COURTING   PROMPTED REMINISCENCE

Some people will enjoy describing how they did their courting.

SOME PROMPTS:

- Where did they meet their partner?
- Who introduced them?
- How long did they know them before they were married?
- Can they remember their first kiss?
- How did they spend their time together?
- Did their friends and parents support or oppose the relationship?
- Did they have to wait and save to get married?

MIND YOU ARE HOME BY ELEVEN!   A DRAMA IDEA

In the past, as now, parents and grown up children had disagreements about appropriate behaviour between boys and girls. Discuss some of the things which were or were not allowed and set up a short dialogue.

Here are some ideas:

- A courting couple on the front door step, with a parent constantly opening the front door to say *'Don't be long!'*.
- A courting couple found by a parent in the front room, kissing.
- A young man calling at a girl's house to take her out and her father telling him how to behave and when to bring his daughter back.

COURTING THEN AND NOW

THEN AND NOW

Encourage a discussion about how the group members behaved as young people, how they think their children behaved, and how young people behave today.

SAVING TO GET MARRIED

READ A QUOTATION

"I was working as a builder's labourer. Money was very scarce. We'd keep our savings in a tin. Sometimes it was three or four bob, sometimes less. We were engaged for four and a half years. You had to court for a long time in order to save up."

See if this memory reminds people of their own experience. Go on to talk about what they saved up to buy and what they thought at the time were the most important things that they should buy.

SEWING FOR THE MARRIAGE

PROMPTED REMINISCENCE

Many women will have sewn and embroidered clothes, linen and other household items ready for their marriage. Ask them what they made and see if they can describe in detail what the items were like. Some people may still have things which they made for their wedding; they may like to show them to the group.

Ask whether they accumulated other household items before getting married.

IN MY BOTTOM DRAWER

ASKING ROUND THE GROUP

Develop the previous discussion by asking everyone in turn to say what they might imagine there would be in a young woman's 'bottom drawer' or 'marriage chest'. Start off with *'I looked in my bottom drawer and I found....'* Some examples: a pair of white sheets, an embroidered dressing table runner, a red and white check drying up cloth.

If members of the group have good memories, turn the activity into a game by asking them to repeat what other people have said before adding their contribution.

WEDDING PHOTOGRAPHS

USING PICTURES

Hand round some wedding photographs, either those brought in by members of the group, your own, a friend's, or some from a newspaper or magazine.

Ask people who were married to describe their own wedding.

WEDDINGS I HAVE BEEN TO

PROMPTED REMINISCENCE

Ask people to describe their memories of a wedding they have been to. Encourage people to share a variety of different sorts of weddings and see how wide a range of experience there is among members of the group.

Some ideas about differences: country or town weddings, many guests or very few guests, Christian, Jewish, Hindu, Moslem, Sikh weddings, a happy couple or an unhappy couple, a very young couple or an older couple.

MY WEDDING OUTFIT

DRAWING ACTIVITY

Either get everyone to draw their wedding clothes trying to remember as much detail as possible.

Or, particularly if some people were not married or have difficulty in drawing, do several large drawings of people and ask the group members about what wedding clothes to draw, include drawings of bridesmaids and pageboys as well. They can make suggestions about what they actually wore or what they would have liked to have worn.

Remember white wedding dresses were not universal even in Britain. In the past, as in many cultures today, it was not unusual for a woman to be married in their best outfit and not in white. In most parts of India red is the bride's colour.

WEDDING CLOTHES   TOUCH AND SEE

Borrow a white wedding dress, a wedding sari, and other wedding clothes to show people and even dress up in.

With the group members, examine what it is made from and how it is made. Look at and feel, for instance, the material, the petticoat, the decorations, the buttons, the stitches.

Discuss the other things a bride might wear, such as a veil, a garland, wedding jewellery, a head dress, special shoes.

WARTIME WEDDINGS   READ A QUOTATION

"My sister got married during the war. You couldn't get cake or anything, and all the dried fruit was on coupons. And as for the wedding dress, she had to borrow one because buying a wedding dress would really cost you. Actually, I think half of Blackheath must have borrowed this dress!"

If anyone in the group got married during the war, this quotation may remind them of the difficulties of having a white wedding dress and providing traditional wedding food. Some people may remember that it was difficult to have wedding photographs taken during the war.

THE DIARY OF MY WEDDING DAY   CREATIVE WRITING

If everyone in the group was married, suggest that people go back over their wedding day and remember it in great detail hour by hour to write it up like a diary.

THE FACTS OF LIFE   PROMPTED MEMORIES/THEN AND NOW

An all-women reminiscence group may be interested in discussing how they learned about sex, what attitudes were like in their family, and issues about contraception.

You could also prompt a discussion about what the group members think about the behaviour of young people today. Encourage them to look carefully at the advantages and disadvantages of the greater level of freedom and knowledge nowadays.

SETTING UP HOME

PROMPTED REMINISCENCE

This topic includes both people who set up home on marriage and people who made their own home without marriage.

Ask them to describe what it was like moving into their new home, what accommodation they had, and what they particularly liked and disliked about it. Ask them about the various rooms, the furniture and furnishings. They may also have something to say about the landlady or landlord, or about sharing with other members of the family.

The difficulties of making ends meet, of keeping out of debt, of buying furniture on hire purchase may also be things they remember.

People who set up home during the war or were bombed out may have memories of having to start collecting furniture and possessions when there were war-time shortages and very little choice.

MY HOME

SHOWING ROUND

Ask someone to show the group around their home as if the group were visitors. The person showing round should be encouraged to remember as much detail as possible, such as the furniture, the colour of the walls, the sort of floor covering, pictures, photographs and ornaments on display.

FURNITURE STYLES °

LOOKING AT PICTURES

If you can borrow a book from the library with pictures of domestic interiors or furniture which covers the thirties and forties, show it to the group and discuss the sort of furniture they had or would have liked to have.

CHANGING TIMES

THEN AND NOW

Ask the group members to discuss the differences between their childhood home and the home they made as an adult. Go on to compare these memories with the homes they had later.

Prompt them with reminders about changes in household equipment used for cooking and keeping food cool, changes in heating, washing and ironing, changing methods of cleaning and changing fashions in furniture and soft furnishings. Ask them when they first had an indoor toilet and a bathroom.

ADVICE TO A YOUNG COUPLE

WRITING

Ask the group members what advice they would give to a young couple about to set up home nowadays. The various pieces of advice could be written down and perhaps given to young members of staff, particularly anyone whom the group knows is about to get married or has recently done so.

12. LIVING THROUGH THE WAR

Before talking about the second world war (1939 - 1945) make a rough calculation about how old group members would have been in 1940, because there will quite a lot of differences between the experience of people who were adults then and the experience of people who were young people or children.

Women who were married or running a home may remember the difficulties of keeping a household going in wartime conditions. Women who were unmarried will probably have had to do war work, perhaps away from home, as men did. Some people who were children will have memories of separations and divided families, others may remember war time as a time of freedom. There will also be a difference between city dwellers affected by bombing and people who lived in the more remote parts of the countryside.

The Second World War made a big impact on the lives not only of people living in Europe, but in other parts of the world as well. Military and civilian war work was undertaken by women and men in many countries outside Europe, including the Caribbean, India, Singapore, as well as the new Commonwealth countries and the United States. Make sure that your discussions do not only concentrate on Britain.

For many people memories of the war are very positive. They focus on the friendliness, the chance to travel, and for women, the opportunity to have a paid job in the forces, in industry, in an office or in transport.

However, some people's memories are painful, involving death, struggles and displacement. You need to be sensitive to people who do not want to be reminded of unhappy memories and give time to people who do want to talk about things which make them sad or angry.

THE DAY WAR BROKE OUT

PROMPTED REMINISCENCE/ STARTING ACTIVITY

In Britain the outbreak of war was announced on Sunday 3rd September 1939 with a broadcast by the prime minister Neville Chamberlain on the wireless. Ask people if they can remember listening to the broadcast and can describe where they were, whom they were with and what they felt at the time. Find out if the broadcast was heard by people not resident in Britain.

There are tape recordings available with the broadcast on it.

THE FIRST AIR RAID WARNING

PROMPTED REMINISCENCE

Immediately after the broadcast at the beginning of the war, the air raid sirens sounded. Ask people if they can remember the sound of the siren and the 'all clear' and what they felt and did the first time.

STARTING WITH OBJECTS

USING OBJECTS/ STARTING ACTIVITY

Make a collection of objects associated with wartime :

- a ration card
- identity card
- gas mask
- pictures of people in uniform,
- a piece of dark cloth representing black out material
- some picture post cards of propaganda posters such as those published by the Imperial War Museum in London
- illustrations from books.

Lay the objects out on a table where they can be seen by everyone and encourage people to talk about the memories that are prompted.

WHAT WE WERE DOING DURING THE WAR

PROMPTED REMINISCENCE

To get a first general idea about the range of people's wartime experience, you could ask them what they were doing in the first year of the war and what they were doing by the end of the war. Some of them may have been in the services, others may have done civilian work, others may have been looking after the home. People may want to go on talking at some length about their wartime experiences once they get started.

WARTIME PRECAUTIONS AT HOME

LISTING ACTIVITY

Ask people to remember some of the many precautions they had to take during wartime. Start the list off by mentioning putting blackout up at all the windows, carrying a gas mask at all times, making a bomb shelter at home under a strengthened table or building one in the garden, and see what other precautions people remember taking.

EVACUATION

READ A QUOTATION

A MOTHER'S MEMORY:

"I had three children who were evacuated with their school. I did not see them off because I was too upset. For the first two days after they went I could not eat. I was so upset about them going. My eldest boy, James, was nearly thirteen, and the others were ten and seven. He would not be parted from the other two and so they were left until last to be chosen. The lady who had them was a marvellous lady and she looked after them very well."

A CHILD'S MEMORY:

"I was nine years old when I was evacuated and my sister was four years older. I can remember quite clearly queuing up in the school yard waiting for the transport. We had an old fashioned paper bag given to us with emergency rations. I remember a big bar of chocolate and a tin of corned beef. We were billeted together because it was always done to keep brothers and sisters together if possible. We went to stay with an elderly couple. My sister says that Mum and Dad came down to visit us by coach, but I cannot remember much about it. I was a little bit homesick and I do remember that I used to wet the bed."

These memories come from '*Good Night Children Everywhere: Memories of Evacuation in World War II',* published by Age Exchange. Within a reminiscence group there may be people who experienced evacuation as children who were evacuated, or as parents who sent their children to be evacuated, or as adult or child hosts. Ask people to talk about their experience and be prepared for some unhappy memories from people for whom the episode is still painful.

TAKING SHELTER   ASKING ROUND THE GROUP

If you have discovered that people in the group did have the experience of going to a shelter, you can ask round the group *'What will you take with you?'*. Explain the activity by saying that if an air raid warning had just gone off and they had to take shelter in a hurry what would be the most important things to take with them.
\
Encourage everyone to say one thing - sensible or funny. Start the ball rolling if necessary with suggestions such as: a flask of tea, a torch, the cat.

TAKING SHELTER   A DRAMA IDEA

After some discussion of being in an air raid shelter, you could set up a few minutes of spontaneous drama. Either pretend that the whole group is in a shelter or have a few people squashed together representing the people in the shelter. Improvise a conversation or argument drawing on suggestions from group members.

RATIONING   PROMPTED REMINISCENCE

Rationing, shopping and queuing were features of the war which many people remember.

SOME PROMPTS:
- ration books
- registering with a butcher
- the number of coupons needed for various items
- shortages of clothing and furniture
- the black market.

The Age Exchange Publication '*Living through the Blitz'* has memories of everyday life of Londoners during the blitz.

WARTIME COOKING   PRACTICAL ACTIVITIES

Ask people what they can remember about cooking and eating during the war. Remind them about carrot cake, eggless and fatless baking, paste sandwiches, spam, Woolton pie, cocoa made with water.

Following a discussion about wartime food, you could do some real cooking. Books about life during the war often reprint recipes, or group members may be able to supply recipes. Make the items to eat, perhaps for a wartime party or VE day celebration.

WARTIME SLOGANS

THINGS LEARNED BY HEART

During the war there were many official propaganda slogans and unofficial catch phrases which became household phrases. See how many the group can remember and write them down.

Discuss what they refer to and whether or not people felt that their behaviour was influenced by them.

SOME EXAMPLES:

- Dig for victory
- Make do and mend
- Coughs and sneezes spread diseases
- Be like dad keep mum
- Careless talk costs lives
- The squander bug
- Stretching your rations
- Salvage your waste paper
- Keep your sunny side up
- Oversexed, overpaid and over here
- It's that man again
- Can I do you now sir?

MAKE DO AND MEND

LISTING

Make a list of the ways people economised on food, clothing, and other household objects.

SOME SUGGESTIONS:

- keeping the ends of bars of soap
- making children's clothes from adults' clothes
- baking cakes without eggs
- turning bed sheets sides to middle.

WARTIME STREET SCENE

DRAWING ACTIVITY

A street scene of houses and back gardens would be an excellent subject for a wartime reminiscence picture. If necessary, you could do the drawing and the reminiscence group could make suggestions about what to put in the picture.

SOME IDEAS

- in the garden : vegetables, chickens
- in the street : air raid shelters, a painted over street sign, the Air Raid Warden coming round on a bicycle, blacked-out or taped-up windows.

WAR WORK

PROMPTED REMINISCENCE

Women without dependant children, as well as men, were required to do work of use to the war effort. This was either in the forces, the civilian services or in occupations which were useful, such as mining, farming or working on the railways.

Ask people to describe what different jobs they had during the war, what the work involved, and where they did it.

The Age Exchange publication **'What Did You Do In The War, Mum?'** is a good source for reminiscences of women's work during the war.

'A Place to Stay', also published by Age Exchange, includes memories of people born outside Britain

WAR WORK

WRITING

A way of encouraging people to remember in more detail would be to suggest that they write a diary for each year of the war, recording changes of job, rank, location, employment and including memories of friends, colleagues and bosses.

IN UNIFORM

DRAWING ACTIVITY

Many people wore military or civilian uniform or distinctive clothing during the war. Provide people with large sheets of paper and see if they can remember the clothes they wore for work. Do the drawings for them from their instructions if this is a better way of concentrating on the memories rather than the drawing.

This activity could be extended to off-duty clothing as well.

AIR RAID PRECAUTIONS

PROMPTED REMINISCENCE

In urban areas many people were involved in the Air Raid Precaution Services, widely known as the A.R.P. either as part-time volunteers or on the receiving end of an A.R.P.'s work.

See if people can remember what the responsibilities of the A.R.P. wardens were or can remember the local A.R.P. wardens and what they were like. There may be some former A.R.P. wardens among the reminiscence group.

The A.R.P wardens were supposed to know their area and its inhabitants thoroughly and give local people advice. They were supposed to be first on the scene of an air raid, summon help, and do what they could till help arrived.

ENTERTAINMENTS

MUSIC

There are many commercially available tapes of the music, entertainers and radio programmes which were important to people during the war.

Play excerpts from a tape and see what else people can remember hearing.

FILMS & TELEVISION

EVERYDAY ACTIVITY

Films made during the war, as well as films about the war, are often shown on television. Look out for relevant films to watch with the group or to video and use excerpts. As well as films with a story, wartime documentary films are also interesting.

Wartime films were often made with an underlying propaganda purpose. This is a good topic for discussion. See if people can remember how they reacted to these films at the time, and what they think of them now.

THE END OF THE WAR

USING PICTURES

Many local oral history publications have pictures of end of the war celebrations and street parties. Use such pictures if you can find them to prompt people to remember how they marked the end of the war.

AFTER THE WAR WAS OVER

PROMPTED REMINISCENCE

Ask the members of the group what life was like after the war and how far things were ever the same again. Prompt with questions about continued shortages, about the return of servicemen, the loss of employment for women, and the introduction of the welfare state.

APPENDICES
1. WAYS OF ASKING QUESTIONS

Many of the ideas in this book are about activities which will stimulate reminiscence, but you will also be involved in prompting people with words. In order to develop a wide range of ways of encouraging people to talk, practise using different methods of prompting people and observe which ones are most effective.

These examples may help you understand how to vary the way you prompt people.

Closed questions invite only a short answer, perhaps only one word:

QUESTION: 'Did you go to school in London?'
ANSWER: 'No.'

If that is the information you need, then you have got it, but if the question was supposed to prompt memories then it probably did not do so, or if it did, you have not invited the reminiscer to tell them to you.

Closed recall questions involve remembering information, but also need only a short answer.

QUESTION: 'How old were you when you left school?'
ANSWER: 'I was 14.'

There are occasions when you want only very brief answers, for instance you may want to know how old everyone in the group was when they left school and not want them at that point to tell you anything else.

Questions which involve remembering precise information are often difficult to answer.

Open questions encourage the respondent to answer in more than one or two words and to choose what they talk about.

PROMPT:
'Tell me what you remember about your school?'
ANSWER:
'Well, I remember the big red brick building and the strict teachers, and my friend Annie'.

This sort of answer gives you a chance to ask some probing questions or comments to encourage more detail.

PROMPT:
'Tell us more about your friend Annie.'
QUESTION:
'You had a friend called Annie?'
QUESTION:
'What can you remember about the school building?'

PROCESS QUESTIONS encourage people to think more deeply about their opinions.

QUESTION:
'Why do you think teachers were so much stricter in those days?' or

'What is different about the opportunities you had from those your grandchildren have?'

AFFECTIVE QUESTIONS draw attention to feelings and attitudes.

Affective questions can be open, closed, recall or process questions.

QUESTION:
'What sorts of feelings do you have when you remember your school days?' (OPEN)

QUESTION:
'Did you like school?' (CLOSED)

QUESTION:
'What was the name of your favourite teacher?' (RECALL)

QUESTION:
'Why do you think that you disliked school so much?' (PROCESS)

Leading questions imply a particular response by the way they are worded and so they may not give people a chance to say what they really think.

QUESTION:
'Everyone had a best friend, what was yours called?'

A leading question can also be a useful way of starting a debate and inviting people to disagree.

QUESTION:
'School days are the best days of your life, aren't they?'

Multiple questions are several questions asked together and can be confusing. Multiple questions may also mean that only one part is answered.

QUESTION: *'Would you like to sit here and tell me about your school days, you were at Barnet Primary weren't you?'*

(Which of the three questions in this statement is the responder to answer?)

2. BOOKS & ARTICLES ABOUT REMINISCENCE

J Adams
'Reminiscence in the Geriatric Ward:
an undervalued resource',
Oral History, vol. 12, no 2 (1984)

'The remembrance of times past',
Geriatric Nursing, July/August (1985) 32-34

S Baines, Saxby & Ehlert
'Reality orientation and reminiscence therapy,
a controlled cross-over study of elderly confused
people'
British Journal of Psychiatry, 151, 222-231
(1987)

M Bender, A Norris, P Bauckham ,
'Groupwork with the Elderly',
Winslow Press (1987)

J Bornat,
'Reminiscence Reviewed',
Open University Press (1993)

R N Butler
'Life review. An interpretation of reminiscence in
the aged',
Psychiatry, 26-76 (1963)

J Carroll
'Piecing it together: life story books',
Community Care, 24 January (1991)

P Coleman
'Ageing and the reminiscence process',
Wiley (1986)

'Ageing and reminiscence: theory and attitude
reviewed',
Geriatric Medicine, 15, October (1987)

F Gibson
'Reminiscence: a handbook for care staff ',
Age Concern (1993)

'Using reminiscence '
Help the Aged (1989)

M Johnson
'That was your life: a biographical approach to
later life'
V Carver & P Liddiard (eds) An Ageing
Population (1978)

G Jones
'The use of recall to reinforce the here and now',
New Age, 25, 12-13 (1984)

G Jones & P Clark
'The use of memory recall on a psychogeriatric
ward',
British Journal of Occupational Therapy,
47,10, 315-316 (1984)

J Kiernat
'The use of life review activity with confused
nursing home residents',
American Journal of Occupational Therapy,
33, 306-10 (1979)

G Langley
'Reminiscence',
in DM Langley, 'Dramatherapy and Psychiatry',
Croom Helm (1983)

N Leng
'A brief review of cognitive behaviour treatments
in old age',
Age and Ageing, 14, 257-263 (1985)

J Lesser, W Lazarus, R Frankel & Havasy
'Reminiscence group therapy with psychotic
geriatric inpatients',
Gerontologist, 21, 291-296 (1981)

C Lewis
'Reminiscing and self-concept in old age',
Journal of Gerontology, 26,12 (1971)

M A Lieberman & S S Tobin
'The Experience of Old Age, Stress, Coping and
Survival',
Basic Books, New York (1983)

J Monkman & A Newton
'Memories are made of this'
Nursing Standard, 2 September 1989, 49, 3

A Norris & A Abu El Eileh
'Reminiscence groups'
Nursing Times, 78, 32, 1368-9 (1982)
reprinted in Oral History, 11, 1 (1983)

A Norris
'Reminiscence',
Winslow Press (1986)
'Reminiscing: a therapeutic role',
Geriatric Medicine, November (1987) 10-13

C Osborn and P Schweitzer
'Lifetimes'
Age Exchange (1987)

P Perotta & J Meacham
'Can a reminiscing intervention alter depression and self-esteem?'
International Journal of Ageing and Human Development, 14, 223-30 (1981)

P Schweitzer
'Age Exchanges : Reminiscence projects for groups of children and older people'
Age Exchange (1993)

P Schweitzer
'Remembering Yesterday, Caring Today'
Reminiscence with people with dementia and their family carers
Age Exchange (1998)

P Schweitzer
'Reminiscence in Dementia Care'
Age Exchange (1998)

S Thornton & J Brotchie '
'Reminiscence - a critical review of the empirical literature'
British Journal of Clinical Psychology, 26, 93-111 (1987)

P Thompson
'The Voice of the Past '
(1978)

C Wheeler & M Growcott
'Reminiscing with elderly patients'
Social Work Today, 6 October 1988

M Wright
'Making History'
Community Care, 646, 23-25 (1987)
'Power of the Past'
Residential Care, 2, 2, 26-27 February (1988)

3. AGE EXCHANGE TRAINING PROGRAMMES

Age Exchange offers a range of short, intensive courses at a variety of skill levels, some held in London and some in other areas on request. All courses encourage active participation and practical work. They are of particular interest to health and social services staff, community arts workers, librarians, teachers and anyone working with and caring for older people.

Courses available include :

- Introduction to reminiscence
- Creative Activities using reminiscence
- Cross-generational reminiscence
- Reminiscence with mentally infirm older people
- Making shows, books and exhibitions from reminiscence
- Transactional analysis and reminiscence
- Nursing and reminiscence.

Details of courses from :
The Reminiscence Co-ordinator,
Age Exchange Reminiscence Centre,
11, Blackheath Village,
London SE3 9LA
Tel. 081 318 9105
Fax 081 318 0060

4. AGE EXCHANGE PUBLICATIONS LIST

It is a feature of all these books that the contributions come from many older people, are lively and easy to read, conversational in style and lavishly illustrated with photographs and line drawings of the time. All the stories are told in the original words of the older people, and make an excellent starter for group or individual reminiscence sessions.

ACROSS THE IRISH SEA (memories of London Irish older people)

A DAY AT THE FAIR (Blackheath Fair in 1920s-40s)

AGE EXCHANGES (reminiscence projects for groups of children and older people)

ALL OUR CHRISTMASES (Christmas memories 1920s-40s)

A PLACE TO STAY (memories of pensioners from many lands)

CAN WE AFFORD THE DOCTOR? (health and social welfare before NHS)

FIFTY YEARS AGO (memories of the 1930s)

FOOTPRINTS IN THE SAND (seaside memories of the 1920s, 30s and 40s)

GOOD MORNING CHILDREN (schooldays in the 1920s and 30s)

GOODNIGHT CHILDREN EVERYWHERE (memories of evacuation in WW II)

GRANDMOTHER'S FOOTSTEPS (book of reflections by older people and children on their grandparents)

JUST LIKE THE COUNTRY (London's inter-war cottage estates)

LIVING THROUGH THE BLITZ (Londoners' memories)

MY FIRST JOB (memories of starting work in the 1920s and 30s)

ON THE RIVER (memories of working on London's river and docks)

OUR LOVELY HOPS (memories of hop-picking in Kent)

REMEDIES AND RECIPES (Caribbean health and diet)

THE TIME OF OUR LIVES (leisure time in the 1920s and 30s)

WHAT DID YOU DO IN THE WAR, MUM? (women's wartime work)

WHEN WE WERE YOUNG (Somerset rural memories)

WINTER WARMERS (memories of coping with winters past)

Prices on request from Books Department,
Age Exchange Reminiscence Centre,
11, Blackheath Village, London SE3 9LA.
Tel. 0181 318 9105

5. AGE EXCHANGE REMINISCENCE BOXES

People who work with or care for older people in residential homes, sheltered housing schemes, day centres and hospitals are using the Age Exchange Reminiscence Boxes to stimulate reminiscence with groups and for one-to-one session work with individuals. Each box contains over 25 objects, sufficient for several sessions, carefully selected from our collection at the Reminiscence Centre and each box has been used and tested by groups of older people.

REMINISCENCE BOXES NOW AVAILABLE FOR HIRE
with some examples of their contents.

1. CHILDHOOD GAMES
Street, playground and rainy day games and rhymes. Older people will enjoy this box. Their younger friends will be fascinated.
Skipping rope, diabolo, spinning top, conkers, marbles, yo-yo, cigarette cards, pea shooter.

2. HOUSEWORK
But what did women do all day at home? This box recalls those endless household chores.
Scrubbing brush, grate polish, cobbler's wax, pumice stone, Robin starch, washing tongs.

3. IN THE KITCHEN
All sorts of kitchen tools and gadgets chosen to recall home cooking, baking and the art of making a little go a long, long way.
Tin opener, fly papers, pastry cutters, apron, bean slicer, whisk, candle, spills, recipes.

4. GOING SHOPPING
Before there were supermarkets and a fridge in every kitchen, most housewives had to do the shopping every day and search for bargains to eke out the housekeeping money.
String bag, groceries, purse, old money, co-op tokens, butter hands, ration book, shopping list.

5. LOOKING GOOD
"We didn't have much, but we knew how to get done up like a dog's dinner in those days."
Make-up, handbag, collars, studs, razor & razor strop, scarf, lace handkerchief, powder compact.

6. AT THE SEASIDE
Memories of outings, trips and holidays on the British riviera!
Sea shells, spade, seaweed, postcards, Brownie box camera, stick of rock, fishing line.

7. WORLD WAR II-THE HOME FRONT
A selection of objects, pictures and documents recalling life in Britain during the War, and how people coped with the changes which War brought.
Newspapers, gas mask, ration book, ARP armband, identity card, blackout material, evacuee label.

8. FAMILY HEALTH

Recalling the days before the NHS began, when preventative medicine and hygiene were a family affair and minor ailments were treated with remedies from the home medicine chest.

Camphorated oil, zinc plasters, castor oil, nappies, chilblain cream, Thermogene wadding.

9. SCHOOL DAYS

Brings back vivid memories of inky fingers and school dinners. The best days of our lives?

Smock, slate, chalk, pen & ink-well, ruler, pea-whistle, geometry set, belt, paper dart, satchel.

10. BORN IN THE CARIBBEAN

Memories of home and social life, food, music and health remedies in the Caribbean islands.

Sugar cane, bay rum, country chocolate, dominoes, carbolic soap, herbs & spices, sarsaparilla, paraffin candles, traditional songs, map of the Caribbean Islands.

11. BORN IN THE INDIAN SUB-CONTINENT

A box developed with a Punjabi Elders Group, recalling childhood, daily life and celebrations.

Incense, wedding garlands, Diwali bowls, perfume oil, henna powder, toy ox-cart, hookah pipe, traditional music.

12. REMINISCENCE STARTER BOX

By public demand!

A box containing a bit of everything! Ideal for people starting up a reminiscence group.

Dolly peg, curling tongs, box camera, Lifebuoy soap, ration book, coins, conkers, stockings, seaweed.

13. PROVERBS, BELIEFS AND SUPERSTITIONS

An assortment of items and a fascinating collection of rhymes and sayings.

Piece of coal, horseshoe, four leaf clover, copper bracelet, wishbone, rabbit's foot, corn dolly.

14. GETTING FROM A TO B: THE TRANSPORT BOX

Memories of transport 1900-1950: Walking, bicycling, motoring, charabancs, trains, buses, air ships, aeroplanes, boats and ships.

Cycle lamp, tram tickets, highway code, spark plugs, AA badge, driving licence, fuel ration book.

15. OFFICE AND SHOP WORK

To stimulate memories of working life and the skills and equipment used in offices and shopwork.

Ready reckoner, pen, bulldog clip, shorthand primer, price tags, adding machine, shirt armbands.

16. MAKE DO AND MEND

A box which recalls the ingenuity of home crafts, repairing and do-it-yourself skills.

Blakeys toe caps, knitting, cellophane jam pot covers, rug hook, wartime recipe book, thrift box, darning box, packet of seeds, hair curling rags, puncture repair kit, elbow patches.

17. VICTORIANA

A collection especially compiled for use in school curriculum history studies. Genuine Victorian objects and documents to bring alive the life and times of Victorian people.

Curling tongs, servant's smock, school "drill" music, woolly combinations, flat iron, ice skates.